NUMBER ONE; REV. ED.

MONTANA GEOGRAPHIC SERIES

BY RICK REESE

PUBLISHED BY

Montana Magazine, Inc.

HELENA, MONTANA 59604

RICK GRAETZ, PUBLISHER
MARK THOMPSON, PUBLICATIONS DIRECTOR
CAROLYN CUNNINGHAM, EDITOR

This series intends to fill the need for in-depth information about Montana subjects. The geographic concept explores the historical color, the huge landscape and the resilient people of a single Montana subject area. Design by Len Visual Design, Helena, Montana. All camera prep work and layout production completed in Helena, Montana. Typesetting by Thurber Printing, Helena, Montana. Printed in Hong Kong by DNP America, San Francisco

PREFACE

It was late December and we were en route to a mountain climbing accident on Mt. Cleveland astride the Montana-Canadian border in Glacier National Park. I had never visited Montana before, but as our plane lumbered northward over the Yellowstone plateau toward Montana that clear winter afternoon, I wasn't interested in the view out the cabin window. I had spent seven years as a climbing ranger in Grand Teton National Park, and even though the area we were flying over contained some of the most wild and magnificent country in all of North America, it was familiar to me.

But as our plane crossed into Montana about 80 miles south of Bozeman, large mountain ranges suddenly loomed up in every direction. There were splendid high peaks and enormous alpine areas surrounded by blankets of forests hundreds of square miles in extent. Although I didn't know it at the time, I was seeing the Madison Range out the left cabin window and the Absaroka Range out the right. Had I not been so taken by the incomparable view, and had I known something of Montana geography, I would also have noticed other ranges as well: the Beartooth beyond the Absaroka to the east, the Crazies and Bridgers to the North, the Tobacco Roots and Pioneers to the west, and the Gallatin Range directly beneath the belly of the plane. And we had just entered Montana — other ranges north of here stretched 300 miles all the way to Canada. Most of the peaks here were not as sharp and crag-like as the Tetons, but these mountains were more extensive and seemed to be truer wilderness ranges, largely roadless and undisturbed. Just before dropping into

A climber beholds the view of Montana's highest mountains from the summit of Wolf Mountain in the Absaroka-Beartooth Wilderness Area. (RICK REESE)

Bozeman to refuel, we passed slighly west of the Spanish Peaks, their deep winter snows bathed in the afternoon sunlight. It was a sight I shall always remember.

My first impression of the vastness of Montana's mountains has been borne out by a decade and a half of familiarity with them. There are indeed few places remaining where the face of the earth has been so little touched by man as in the mountains of Montana; in the lower 48 states nothing exceeds them in wilderness quality or extent. These remnant symbols of our past are indeed the best of what's left of the wild and open America that once was.

But Montana's wild mountains have escaped the ravages of "development" and exploitation only partially because of the geographical accident that placed them so far from the population centers and markets of the nation. Of equal importance, especially in the past few decades, have been the efforts of dedicated conservationists who early recognized the priceless value of western wilderness and who were willing to fight for its preservation. As early as 1931, National Forest primitive areas were established in Montana. These areas were the precursors of the National Wilderness Preservation System that came to fruition with the passage of the Wilderness Act of 1964. But it has been *since* the passage of that law that most of the hard-fought battles to preserve the few remaining wild areas of Montana and American have been fought. Today the battle has reached fever pitch as final decisions are about to be made that will forever seal the fate of millions of acres of roadless Montana back country.

When white man first settled here, the entire 93 million acres of what is now the state of Montana was wilderness. Scarcely a century later, 90 percent of that wilderness domain has been settled, logged, mined, roaded, drilled, dammed and otherwise "developed."

Today only about 10 percent of Montana remains in a roadless and undeveloped condition. Only one third of this country is currently protected in national parks and in Forest Service wilderness areas — the majority of roadless country is still unprotected. Of that which is unprotected, federal agencies have recommended that most of it be opened to new roads and development. In the last six years alone, more than half a million acres of roadless federal lands in Montana have fallen to the mark of man and his civilization.

Today, in 1985, the people of the United States still have an opportunity to bring the protection of congressional wilderness designation to some of the choicest parcels of wild America; but that opportunity is fleeting and must be seized shortly or it will disappear. We can never increase the finite treasure of pristine wildlands with which Montana has been endowed — we can only diminish it. Our generation now bears the responsibility of deciding once and for all how much of that remnant of true wilderness that still remains in Montana will be passed on to our descendents.

Anti-wilderness forces have posed the question "How much wilderness can we afford?" A half-century ago Bob Marshall noted that the American wilderness, even then, was "disappearing like a snowbank on a hot June day." Now in 1985 we are approaching the moment of truth. Once our wildlands are gone we cannot create them anew; they are gone forever. The question that Americans should be asking today is not "How much wilderness can we afford?" but rather "How much more wilderness can we afford to lose?"

Rick Reese

Contributors

Rick Reese was a climbing ranger in Grand Teton National Park before migrating north to Montana, a decade and a half ago, where he has hiked and climbed throughout the mountains of the state. He is a member of the American Alpine Club and has authored numerous articles about Montana and the west. Reese served as director of the Yellowstone Institute from 1980 to 1984 and is the author of the sixth volume in the Montana Geographic Series, *Greater Yellowstone: The National Park and Adjacent Wildlands.*

Rick Graetz is publisher of *Montana Magazine* and has published two photography books on Montana. He is a partner in the outfitting firm of High Country Adventures and has hiked and climbed throughout the mountains of Montana. Graetz has served on the board of directors of the Montana Wilderness Association and has been actively involved in wilderness and conservation affairs for many years. He is the author of the recently-published *Montana's Bob Marshall Country.*

Ed Madej is a Helena cartographer with an extensive first-hand familiarity with the geography of Montana. He is a past president of the Montana Wilderness Association and has collaborated on a number of books about Montana's wild country.

Dave Alt has served on the geology faculty of the University of Montana for 19 years and has published a variety of books and articles on the geology of the northern Rockies. He received his Ph.D. from the University of Texas and taught geology in England and Florida before joining the faculty at the University of Montana.

Stewart Aitchison has had 18 years experience as a field biologist and has authored more than 60 scientific and popular articles. His recent books include *A Naturalist's Guide to the Grand Canyon, A Floater's Guide to the San Juan River,* and *Oak Creek Canyon and the Red Rock Country of Arizona.* Aitchison served on the staff of the Museum of Northern Arizona for 10 years and currently is an interpretive naturalist for Lindblad Special Expeditions.

Wayne Phillips is a range management specialist with the U.S. Forest Service in Great Falls, Montana. He has a degree in forestry and began his Forest Service career as a smokejumper 20 years ago. Phillips teaches botany courses at the College of Great Falls and the Yellowstone Institute. His special interest is mountain botany and he is intimately familiar with the mountains of Montana.

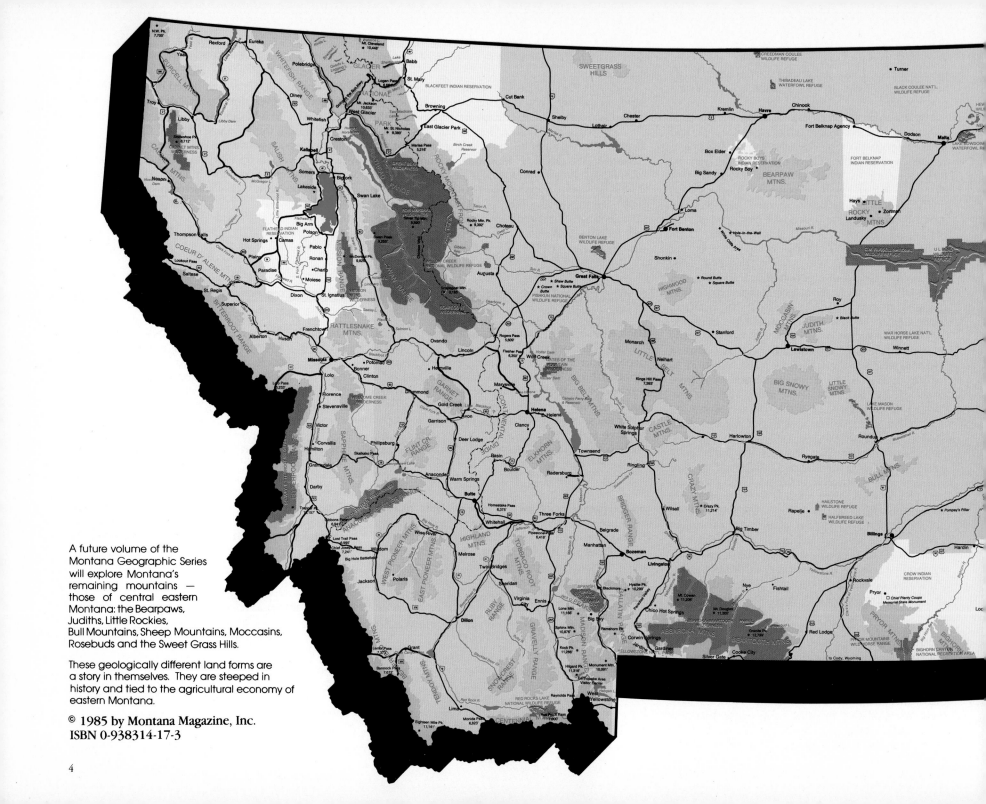

A future volume of the Montana Geographic Series will explore Montana's remaining mountains — those of central eastern Montana: the Bearpaws, Judiths, Little Rockies, Bull Mountains, Sheep Mountains, Moccasins, Rosebuds and the Sweet Grass Hills.

These geologically different land forms are a story in themselves. They are steeped in history and tied to the agricultural economy of eastern Montana.

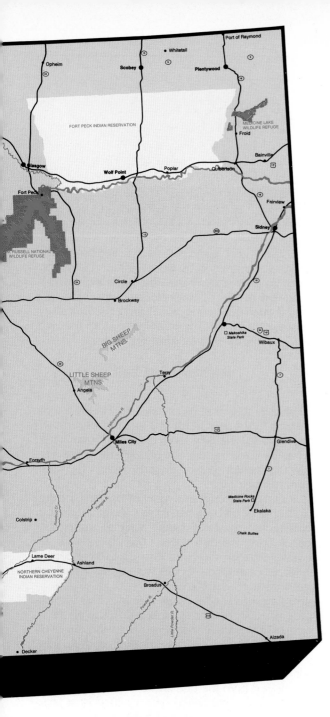

MONTANA Mountain Ranges

CONTENTS

CHAPTER ONE

MONTANA MOUNTAIN GEOLOGY

by Dave Alt

Above Larch Hill Pass looking south along the Chinese Wall, which is a massive limestone escarpment in the so-called overthrust belt. (RICK GRAETZ)

The major geologic events that created Montana's mountains happened between 75 and 45 million years ago — we can be sure that the basic bedrock framework of most of our present mountains already existed when that period ended. Since then, the slow processes of erosion have sculptured the intricate details of our modern mountain landscapes.

The Overthrust Belt

Consider first the mountains of northwestern Montana in the area north of a line drawn through Missoula and Helena and west of the Rocky Mountain Front. The eastern part of that region is the overthrust belt, the western part is the area from which the overthrust belt came.

Evidently, the westernmost part of Montana and the panhandle of Idaho began to rise about 75 million years ago as masses of granite magma invaded the earth's crust beneath them. The thick stack of sedimentary rocks that had accumulated there during hundreds of millions of years were raised and tilted gently down toward the east.

Imagine those sedimentary formations as a thick stack of heavily buttered pancakes on a slightly tilted platter. Great slabs of sedimentary rock thousands of feet thick peeled off one after the other and slid tens of miles eastward into the portion of the overthrust belt now known as the Sawtooth Range. There, each slab lapped onto the one ahead like shingles on a roof. All of this happened over a period of at least several million years, and the movement was so majestically slow that we could hardly have perceived it had we been here then.

Glacial runoff on Great Northern Mountain. (D.J. SMITH)

The dramatic gouging of Grinnell Glacier has left behind a string of mountain lakes in Glacier National Park. Active glaciers exist in several of the state's ranges, but all are mere shrunken remnants of far more extensive rivers of ice that have profoundly shaped the face of Montana in recent geologic times. (RON GLOVAN)

The moving slabs of sedimentary rocks came to rest in the region between the Mission Range and the Rocky Mountain Front to the east. Here the landscape consists of long ridges and valleys that trend generally from north to south. Each ridge is the upturned edge of a slab of resistant sedimentary rocks, each valley marking the outcrop of rocks that weather and erode more easily. Almost every ridge indicates one of the great slabs that slid east.

West of the Mission and Flathead valleys the mountains of northwestern Montana consist mostly of sedimentary rocks that were once very deeply buried. Apparently, the rocks in the overthrust belt to the east slid off this region, stripping it down to the deeper levels of rock we see exposed there today.

The Big Detachment Blocks

The Garnet, Flint Creek, and Anaconda Ranges of central western Montana lie along an approximately semi-circular arc that encloses a region geologists call "the Sapphire Block." This block probably slid eastward for about 50 miles as a single mass from Idaho into Montana. The rumpled edges of the block form the half circle arc of mountains that now defines its borders. The Bitterroot Valley forms the gap behind the trailing western edge of the Sapphire Block.

The Bitterroot Mountains that extend into Idaho west of the Sapphire block consist mostly of granite, and igneous rock that intruded the depths of the earth's crust and then crystallized. Much of the granite in the Bitterroot Mountains is between 75 and 70 millions years old. Its emplacement as magma probably bulged the earth's crust enough to start the Sapphire Block sliding, and its age probably tells us when the block moved.

Although the evidence is less clear, the Pioneer Range of southwestern Montana appears to be another large block that slid off the granite in Idaho and moved east. Its eastern edge is crumpled into tight folds similar to those around the margin of the Sapphire Block. The Big Hole Valley is the gap that opened behind the Pioneer Block.

Rock Creek canyon near the eastern edge of the Beartooth Mountains was carved by an immense glacier that spilled down from the ice-covered Beartooth Plateau during the last ice age. (GEORGE WUERTHNER)

The Boulder Batholith

Most of the rocks exposed in the maze of mountains between Helena and the northern Highland Range south of Butte belong to an enormous mass of granite, called the Boulder batholith, and the volcanic rocks associated with it. Between about 75 and 70 million years ago, this region was probably an enormous volcanic center similar in many respects to the one now active in the Yellowstone Park area. Subsequent erosion removed much of the original volcanic cover, laying bare large expanses of the granite which had crystallized beneath.

The Fault Block Ranges

Most of the mountain ranges of southwestern Montana consist essentially of large segments of the earth's crust raised along faults. Those raised blocks include the Ruby, Snowcrest, Greenhorn, Gravelly, Blacktail, Tendoy, and Madison Ranges, as well as the Beartooth Plateau. The intervening basins such as the Beaverhead, Ruby, Jefferson, Centennial, and Gallatin valleys are similar blocks that dropped along faults as the mountains between them rose.

The fault block ranges of southwestern Montana contain large areas of basement rock, extremely ancient crystalline rocks that comprise the bulk of the continental crust. Basement rocks consist mostly of complex assortments of pinkish granites and streaky gneisses and schists, colorful rocks full of glittering crystals. Most are about 2.7 billion years old — some are more than 3 billion years old. Younger sedimentary rocks cover the ancient basement complex in parts of all the block mountain ranges of southwestern Montana. Still younger volcanic rocks erupted about 50 million years ago and also cover parts of some of those blocks.

Bulges in the Plains of Central Montana

The eastern front of the overthrust belt forms a high wall that firmly defines the western limit of the plains, but without defining the eastern limit of the mountains. Throughout central Montana isolated groups of mountains rise from the plains. In Montana, one cannot draw a sharp line between the plains and the mountains.

Most of those isolated central Montana ranges, the Big Belt, Little Belt, Big Snowy, and Pryor Mountains consist of broad domes arched in the earth's crust. Others, such as the Bridger Range, are more sharply folded. All have old rocks exposed in their cores and younger rocks around their edges which comprise a crude bullseye pattern. It seems likely that this folding also occurred about 50 million years ago.

Volcanoes

Also about 50 million years ago, give or take 5 million years, most of the western half of Montana saw some kind of volcanic activity. One large chain of volcanoes similar to the modern Cascades extended from the area near Livingston south through the eastern part of Yellowstone National Park, and beyond. There were high volcanic peaks in that chain and they covered large areas of the Absaroka and Gallatin Ranges with a deep blanket of volcanic rocks. These volcanoes buried the famous petrified forests of Yellowstone Park and nearby areas.

Another impressive chain of volcanoes erupted along a line extending from the area of the Boulder batholith southwestward through Idaho. Those vents heaped great piles of light-colored volcanic rocks on top of the mountains of the Boulder batholith and across several of the fault block ranges of southwestern Montana. Much of that rock is white rhyolite ash which formed in the violent explosive eruptions.

Meanwhile, molten magma rose into many of the uplifts arched in the plains. In some areas it erupted to form large volcanoes perched on top of the uplift. In others, magma intruded the rocks below the surface. Today we see those igneous intrusions standing high in bold relief because the less resistant sedimentary rocks that once enclosed them have eroded away. In several areas some of the rising magma erupted to form volcanoes, while the rest crystallized below the surface to form intrusions.

The Adel, Highwood, and Bearpaw Mountains consist mostly of the deeply eroded remnants of large volcanoes along with much smaller quantities of intrusive rocks. All three ranges consist largely of rare potassium-rich dark igneous rock. Similar rocks exist in the Crazy Mountains but these rocks are rich in sodium, and they crystallized entirely below the

Glossary

(from Glossary of Geology, 2nd ed., 1980 courtesy Montana Bureau of Mines and Geology, Geologic Map Series 27)

Arete — A narrow serrate mountain crest of rocky, sharp-edged ridge or spur, commonly present above the snowline in rugged mountains (as in the Swiss alps), sculptured by glaciers and resulting from the continued backward growth of the walls of the adjoining cirques.

Bastion — A knob or mass of bedrock projecting into a main glacial valley at the junction with a hanging valley, at or below the level of the hanging-valley floor.

Bergschrund — A deep and often wide gap or crevasse, or a series of closely spaced crevasses, in ice or firn at or near the head of an *alpine glacier* or snowfield, that separates moving ice and snow from the relatively immobile ice and snow (*ice apron*) adhering to the confining headwall of a cirque.

Cirque — A deep, steep-walled, half-bowl-like recess or hollow, variously described as horseshoe-shaped or semicircular in plan, situated high on the side of a mountain, commonly at the head of a glacier valley, and produced by the erosive activity of a mountain glacier.

Cirque glacier — A small glacier occupying a *cirque*, or resting against the headwall of a cirque. It is the most common type of glacier in the mountains of the western United States.

Cirque stairway — A succession of cirques situated in a row at different levels in the same glacial valley.

Col — (a) A high, narrow, sharp-edged *pass* or depression in a mountain range, generally across a ridge or through a divide, or between two adjacent peaks; a deep pass formed by the headward erosion and intersection of two cirques, as in the French Alps. Also, the highest point on a divide between two peaks. (b) A marked, saddle-like depression in the crest of a mountain ridge; the lowest point on a ridge. (c) A short ride or elevated neck of land connecting two larger and higher masses.

Couloirs — A French term for a passage in a cave, or vertical clefts in a cliff.

Faceted spurs — A spur or ridge with an inverted-V face that was produced by faulting or by the trimming, beveling or truncating action of streams, waves or glaciers.

Glacial basin — A rock basin caused by erosion of the floor of a glacial valley.

Glacial-lobe lake — A lake occupying a depression that was excavated by a glacial lobe as it advanced over the drainage basin of a former river.

Glacial stream — A flow of water that is supplied by melting glacier ice; a meltwater stream.

Glacial terrace — A terrace formed by glacial action, either by arranging glacial materials in terrace form (such as a remnant of a valley train), or by cutting into bedrock.

Glacial trough — A deep, steep-sided, U-shaped valley leading down from a cirque, and excavated by an alpine glacier that has widened, deepened and straightened a preglacial river valley.

Hanging tributary — A tributary stream or tributary glacier occupying a *hanging valley*.

Hanging valley — A glacial valley whose mouth is a relatively high level on the steep side of a larger glacial valley. The larger valley was eroded by a trunk glacier and the smaller one by a tributary glacier, and the discordance of level of their floors, as well as their difference in size, is due to the greater erosive power of the trunk glacier.

Headwall — A steep slope at the head of a valley; the rock cliff at the back of a cirque.

Horn — A high, rocky, sharp-pointed mountain peak with prominent faces and ridges, bounded by the intersecting walls of three or more cirques that have been cut back into the mountain by headward erosion of glaciers; e.g. the Matterhorn of the Pennine Alps.

Lateral moraine — (a) A low, ridgelike moraine carried on, or deposited at or near, the side margin of a mountain glacier. It is composed chiefly of rock fragments loosened from the valley walls by glacial abrasion and plucking, or fallen onto the ice from the bordering slopes. (b) An end moraine built along the side margin of a glacial lobe occupying a valley.

Névé — A French term meaning a mass of hardened snow at the source or head of a glacier; it refers to the overall snow cover that exists during the melting period and sometimes from one year to another. The term was originally used in English as an exact equivalent of *firn* (the material) and is still frequently so used, but it is perhaps best to restrict it, as proposed by British glaciologists, to a geographic meaning, such as an area covered with perennial snow or an area of firn (a *firn field*), or more generally the accumulation area above or at the head of a glacier.

Outwash-plain shoreline — A prograding shoreline formed where the outwash plain in front of a glacier is built out into the lake.

Talus slope — A step, concave slope formed by an accumulation of loose rock fragments; especially such a slope at the base of a cliff, formed by the coalescence of several rockfall taluses or alluvial taluses.

Tarn — a relatively small and deep, steep-banked lake or pool amid high mountains, especially one occupying an ice-gouged rock basin amid glaciated mountains.

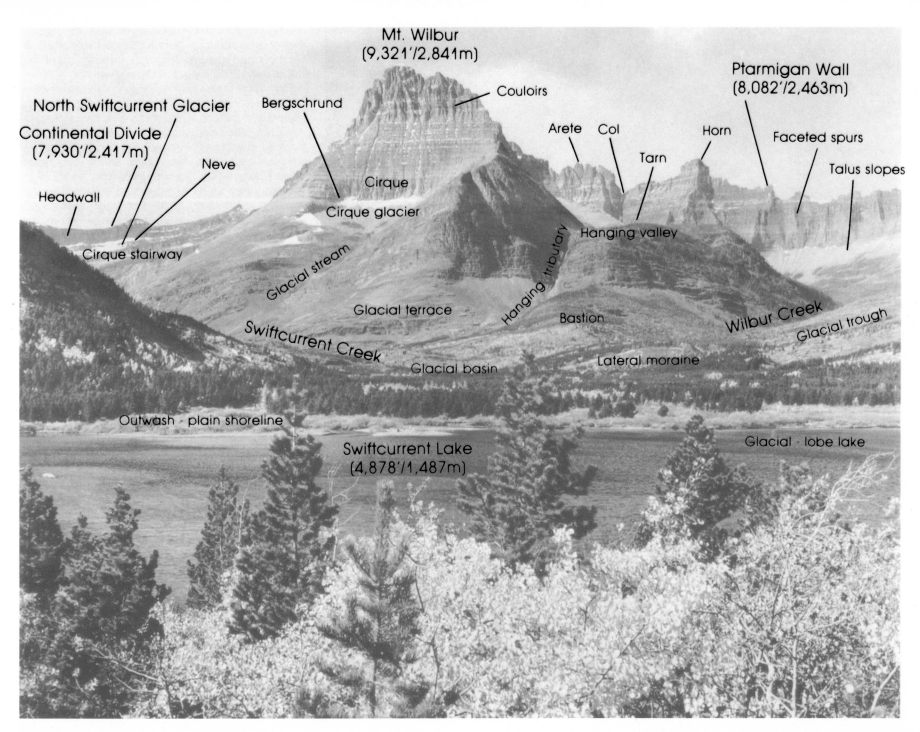

Mt. Wilbur
(9,321'/2,841m)

North Swiftcurrent Glacier

Continental Divide
(7,930'/2,417m)

Ptarmigan Wall
(8,082'/2,463m)

Bergschrund

Couloirs

Neve

Arete

Col

Horn

Faceted spurs

Headwall

Tarn

Talus slopes

Cirque

Cirque glacier

Cirque stairway

Glacial stream

Hanging valley

Hanging tributary

Glacial terrace

Bastion

Wilbur Creek

Swiftcurrent Creek

Glacial trough

Glacial basin

Lateral moraine

Outwash - plain shoreline

Glacial - lobe lake

Swiftcurrent Lake
(4,878'/1,487m)

Right: a climber views a steep couloir carved by the relentless forces of erosion. (RICK REESE) *Below: a rock glacier, which is a matrix of rock and ice that behaves like a glacier, creeps toward the forest edge in the Madison Range.* (WAYNE PHILLIPS)

surface. In the Crazy Mountains, erosion of the much softer surrounding rocks left the igneous intrusions of the range standing high and forming one of the most spectacular ranges in the region.

The Sweetgrass Hills, Judith and Moccasin Mountains, and Little Rocky Mountains contain igneous intrusions in the crests of domes arched in the crust, but there are no volcanoes present in this area. Similar igneous intrusions exist in the north end of the Little Belt Mountains. As in the Crazy Mountains, those igneous intrusions stand high because they are more resistant to erosion than the weaker sedimentary rocks that once surrounded them. The Castle Mountains may also belong in this group with the qualification that some volcanic activity did occur there.

After the Main Action

Volcanic activity and crustal movements diminished greatly in Montana about 45 million years ago, and erosion has since played the major role in shaping our mountains. For millions of years streams have relentlessly carved Montana's mountains, patiently reshaping them into new forms. Mountains that consist of volcanic rock, for example, now show no sign of their original volcanic forms but consist simply of an erosional landscape carved into volcanic rocks.

Ice ages have come and gone many times during the last 2 or 3 million years. Great glaciers have left their mark where they gouged the valleys of the higher ranges. Signs of ice age glaciation are evident in the higher mountains. Look for them on the peaks that catch the clouds and make their own weather, high on the serrated skyline of craggy peaks that rise steeply above deeply gouged valleys.

The geologic story of Montana's mountains isn't over. Occasional earthquakes in western Montana show that crustal movements continue throughout the region. As recently as 1959 parts of the Madison Range rose about 15 feet during the Hebgen earthquake; Yellowstone National Park contains an enormous volcano that will likely erupt again; and it is probably safe to assume that the future will bring more ice ages and more great glaciers to further shape our higher ranges. We can be sure that the patient processes of erosion will continue to carve new details into Montana's mountains.

EARTHQUAKE

Late on the night of August 17, 1959 a tremendous earthquake rumbled through the southern end of the Madison Range, shaking loose one of the largest North American landslides in historic times. The quake, centered near Hebgen Lake, was felt as far as 350 miles away. It ruptured a basaltic dike causing the collapse of an entire mountainside into the Madison River. Hebgen Lake itself was tilted more than 20 feet; the Madison Range rose several feet and more than 18 miles of fault scarp occurred. Twenty-eight persons camped here on that fateful night lost their lives, most of them buried forever under millions of cubic yards of broken rock and mud. In this aerial photo the enormous slide can be seen filling the Madison Canyon, damming the river, and burying the entire highway except for a small portion visible in the extreme bottom center of the picture. The photo below shows the same stretch of highway from the canyon bottom. Note the depth of the slide, which started on the right, ran all the way across the canyon and far up the left slope.

(U.S. FOREST SERVICE PHOTOS)

CHAPTER TWO

MOUNTAIN VEGETATION

by Wayne Phillips

Wildflowers on Red Mountain south of Butte. (RON GLOVAN)

Montana's mountain vegetation is as varied as its landscape. Golden grasslands contrast with deep green coniferous forests, purple hills of sagebrush blend with lush mountain meadows, and on alpine ridges yellow lilies push through brilliant snowbanks.

Variations in Montana's mountain vegetation result from environmental differences such as elevation, landform, soil and geologic substrata, direction and steepness of slope, climate and precipitation, and wind patterns. These differences are reflected in corresponding variations in vegetation, but the mosaic of shrubland, grassland, forest and meadow is not as haphazard as it may appear. It is nature's expression of its contrasting environments.

Other conditions contributing to changes in vegetation result from disturbance factors. Fire, insect epidemic, logging, grazing by wild and domestic animals, landslides and snowslides, windstorms and other conditions and events produce corresponding changes in the plant communities. Lightning-caused wildfire, for example, has been a major factor in shaping the vegetation patterns in Montana since the retreat of the glaciers. Following the catastrophic disturbance of wildfire, a burned area becomes a seedbed offering favorable growing conditions for numerous wildflowers, shrubs, and trees. The early, fast growing plants that invade the burn are called the "pioneer" species. These plants benefit from the increased sunlight and nutrients on the burned area. The stately western larch is an example of a pioneer tree whose seeds germinate and prosper in the openings in the forest provided by fire, avalanche, or similar disturbance. Lodgepole pine, fireweed, aspen, cheatgrass, and serviceberry are other examples of pioneer plants.

As the forest matures the pioneer species are replaced in succession by slower-growing and longer-lived plants — plants that are more tolerant of the dense forest shade. The more stable and longer-lived plant community that develops as the forest matures is referred to as the "climax" forest. Sub-alpine fir, western red cedar, and hemlock represent the climax stage of plant succession on many forests the mountains of Montana. In other areas, however, and depending on the sum of the environmental

A wide variety of environmental and climatic conditions across Montana supports diverse vegetative communities. Top: Fireweed. (RON GLOVAN)
Bottom: Bitterroot. (CHARLES KAY)
Right: Giant cedars grow to hundreds of years of age in the moist forests west of the Continental Divide. (GEORGE WUERTHNER)

High in the Cabinet Mountains, the rigors of life in the subalpine zone can be seen in frost kill at the tops of coniferous trees. Beargrass blooms despite it all. (GEORGE WUERTHNER)

carpet of Douglas fir and lodgepole pine with an occasional patch of aspen. Low shrubs such as snowberry and ninebark are scattered beneath the trees. Higher yet are the cool, moist forests of sub-alpine fir, spruce and lodgepole pine. Beneath these trees are low shrubs such as huckleberry or, where very moist, taller shrubs such as alder and false huckleberry. Near timberline the forest thins out; whitebark pine dominates the stunted woodland, while sub-alpine fir and spruce barely hang on in the hostile environment. Trees finally give way to alpine tundra with its grasses, sedges and wildflowers. The few trees which do grow in this zone are often trimmed by wind-borne ice crystals into a compact hedge of "Krummholz" only a foot or two high.

As you go north and west across the Continental Divide, Pacific rainfall patterns have an increasing effect on the climate and vegetation. The moist forests of northwestern Montana have much in common with the rain forest on the west slope of the Cascades in Washington and Oregon. If you were to travel from east to west over Marias Pass near Glacier Park, for example, you would see the dramatic influence of this Pacific moisture. East of the Divide the forests are typical of central Montana and the cool, dry, continental-climate influence zone. Lodgepole pine and Douglas fir dominate, while the underbrush is relatively low and sparse. But after crossing the Continental Divide and dropping west toward the Middle Fork of the Flathead River you enter another world. Here the climate is characteristic of the moist maritime zone. Dense forests of western red cedar, grand fir, larch, white pine and Douglas fir are supported by much heavier rainfall. Under tall trees, or in disturbed openings, you will find low trees and tall shrubs such as paper birch, Pacific yew, mountain ash, willow and mountain maple. Beneath that is a third layer of medium shrubs such as thimbleberry and blue huckleberry. Floral variety and vegetation density are characteristic of this moist moderate climate.

The variety of plant life in Montana's mountains offers something for every taste. From the open valley grasslands and neighboring forests of the southwest portion of the state to the lush forest vegetation of the northwest, this vast mountain country provides a rich and varied floral beauty.

factors on a site, climax vegetation may be grassland, shrubland or forest.

Of all the variables affecting climax vegetation, altitude is the most obvious. In southwestern Montana a fisherman casting a fly on the Madison River (elevation 5,000 feet) can glance east to Cedar Mountain (elevation 10,421 feet) and see six major vegetation zones from grassland all the way to alpine tundra. At the base of the mountain, native wheatgrasses and fescues give way to open woodlands of limber pine, juniper and Douglas fir. Farther up the slope forests thicken to a continuous

a) An ancient forest monarch surrounded by alpine larch. (RON GLOVAN)

b) One of the forest's loveliest wildflowers, the blue columbine. (JAN WASSINK)

c) Living low to the ground to conserve energy is the alpine buttercup. (DAVID DAVISON)

d) A welcome sight on a late spring hike, a patch of bearing huckleberries. (RICK GRAETZ)

e) Hoarfrost on alpine larch. (CHARLES KAY)

FIRE

Fire, long regarded as the unequivocal enemy of the forest, is now recognized as a natural force in the ecosystem and essential for the growth of many plant species. On hundreds of thousands of acres of national forest and park lands, fire is allowed to assume its natural role and to run its course under certain environmental conditions. Many species of plants occur only in post-fire environments, where increased sunlight and reduced competition for nutrients contribute to the growth of shrubs, wildflowers and vigorous stands of new trees. In the photos at right an extremely hot fire races through heavy lodgepole fuel on the Bitterroot National Forest. Other natural events, such as the snow-slide path in Glacier Park pictured below, and wind storms, also clear patches of forest cover and contribute to the creation of diverse plant communities.

(U.S. FOREST SERVICE)

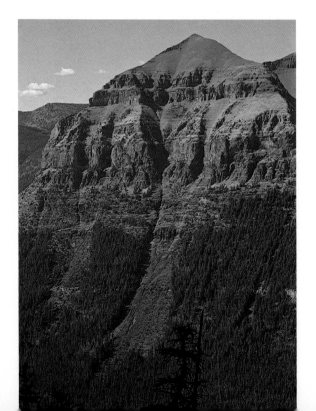

Left: (JIM ROBBINS)
Right: A Forest Service smokejumper bails out over western Montana.
(ALAN CAREY)

Ponderosa pine, Montana's state tree. (GEORGE WUERTHNER)

Whitebark pine in the Beartooths. (GEORGE WUERTHNER)

19

CHAPTER THREE

MOUNTAIN WILDLIFE

by Stewart Aitchison

The mountain goat is rarely seen, but flourishes in many ranges of Montana. In Glacier Park, goats such as this one are easily photographed. Unlike the headset of bighorn sheep, whose charging displays rarely inflict injury, the pitchfork prongs of the goat can gore deeply. (RON GLOVAN)

When the Lewis and Clark expedition came up the Missouri River nearly two centuries ago, it observed, and in some cases collected, samples of most of the major animal species then found in the northern Rockies. Thus, for the first time, the enormous variety of odd and assorted creatures of what is now Montana became known to the people of America.

As the West was settled, these animals had to compete with livestock, endure new diseases and seek refuge from hunters. Populations of many animals including beaver, moose and deer were drastically decimated. Human presence also resulted in behavioral adaptations. Elk, grizzly bear and coyote left the prairies and valleys and moved into the mountains where they sought the protection afforded by the rugged terrain. Fortunately this century has seen the initiation of improved game management, and the future of many species now seems brighter. Transplanting, carefully planned hunting, and in a few cases, even occasional artificial feeding have encouraged the recovery of many game animals.

Vegetative communities are one of the key factors in determining animal distribution, and in the mountains of Montana there are basically four major plant communities: the alpine, boreal, montane and meadow.

The alpine zone is at the highest elevation and is the most ecologically demanding of these plant communities. Here, above timberline, is an environment of intense sunlight, severe cold, dry winds and short growing seasons. Animals living in this ecosystem have had to evolve ingenious means to survive. Alpine insects and other invertebrates (animals without backbones), for example, have developed long life cycles that stretch over several

Right: A moose feeds in the tranquil sanctuary of a forest pond. (CHARLES KAY)

Below: Perhaps the mountaineer's most vocal friend, the pika or "rock rabbit," is known for his friendly shrill whistle. The pika inhabits rocky slopes at and above timberline. Unlike his cottontail relations, the pika has short, rounded ears, front and rear legs of about equal length, and lacks a visible tail. (TIM CHRISTIE)

seasons. In this manner only a certain small segment of the life cycle needs to be completed during the short summer. Since most bees cannot withstand cold temperatures, alpine flies become important pollinators; in classic synergy the continued survival of alpine plants entails providing a food source for insects, and for other animals as well.

Some animals, such as marmots, hibernate to avoid the rigors of winter in this life zone, while others migrate downward to the more moderate environment of the forest. But here deep snow may preclude movement and the finding of suitable forage. The pika, a short-eared relative of the rabbit, remains active under the snowpack during the winter, feeding off its "haystacks" of vegetation gathered the previous summer. The pocket gopher remains underground year-round where burrowing activity helps recycle minerals, distribute seeds, and aerate the thin, friable, alpine soil.

Clockwise from above: Autumn in the mountains brings the annual dominance battles among males — here mule deer test each other. (MICHAEL FRANCIS) *Silent, stealthy, seldom seen — the mountain lion still frequents Montana mountains.* (ED WOLFF) *Not technically a hibernator, black bear succumbs to a deep winter sleep.* (TOM ULRICH) *Predator of the upper forest story, the barred owl.* (TOM ULRICH)

Mountain goats occupy the high, rugged mountain ridges where they surpass the agility of even the human mountaineer. The goat was formerly restricted to the major mountain ranges of western Montana but a transplant program begun in the 1940s has introduced the beast to nearly every range in the state.

Another inhabitant of the rocky cliffs is the bighorn sheep. Sometimes confused with the goat, the bighorn lacks the shaggy wool coat and spike horns. Instead, sheep have relatively short hair and mature rams have horns that curl. Bighorns are now making a comeback after near-extinction from hunting and diseases introduced from domestic sheep.

There are a few birds that nest on the alpine tundra; they include ptarmigan, water pipits, horned larks, rosy finches and white-crowned sparrow. These birds will often be seen gleaning insects and seeds from old snowbanks. Patrolling the skies but nesting in the forest are ravens, hawks, golden eagles, falcons, gray and Steller's jays and Clark's nutcrackers.

The food chain of the alpine ecosystem is relatively simple. For example, alpine clover is eaten by meadow vole, which in turn is eaten by weasel or hawk. But this simplicity means that the system can be easily disrupted. It is a harsh environment and a very fragile one too.

Below the alpine zone are found one of two very general forest types: boreal or montane. Their occurrence depends on elevation, slope, exposure to the sun, prevailing winds and other factors. The boreal forest is the wetter of the two and usually contains species of fir, spruce, and perhaps red cedar and hemlock. It is in this moist forest that one finds such animals as moose, wolverine, fisher, black bear, wood warblers and grouse.

The drier (and usually lower) montane forest is characterized by pine and Douglas fir. Here lion, elk, mule deer and grizzly bear are frequently found. There is, of course, a great deal of overlap as animals range between these two communities; few are restricted to one zone.

The fourth type of plant community is the meadow. Here, at the interface between meadow and forest (called "forest-edge") is the greatest density

Above left: Ptarmigan, one of the few year-round bird residents of the high country, here camouflaged in winter white. (TIM CHRISTIE)
Above: Bighorn rams live in bands and rarely leave traditional ranges. (TOM ULRICH)
Left: Moose are specially adapted for life near lakes and streams. (TOM ULRICH)

23

Enlightened game management policies and preservation of wild land have contributed to the abundant elk herds of Montana. (MONTANA DEPARTMENT OF FISH, WILDLIFE AND PARKS PHOTO)

The joys of the hunt. More than 90,000 hunters take to the hills each year to hunt elk in Montana. About 14 percent are successful in taking what is regarded as one of the world's most challenging and prized big-game animals. (GEORGE WUERTHNER PHOTO)

and diversity of wildlife. Many animals find sustenance in the meadow plants and protection and shelter in the timber.

The much feared grizzly bear is sometimes encountered along the forest edge. The bear, when given a chance, will almost always avoid humans. It needs large tracts of undisturbed wilderness to survive and Montana is fortunate to have the largest remaining grizzly population in the United States outside of Alaska. Surprisingly, grasses and sedges make up most of the diet of this large creature, but it also eats carrion, fruit, pine nuts, roots and other animals. In fact, the grizzly is an opportunistic feeder that will eat almost anything.

Other animals likely to be observed along the forest-edge are ground and red squirrels, porcupine, marten and snowshoe hares. Flickers, Lewis' woodpeckers, hairy woodpeckers, western flycatchers, various warblers, chickadees, nuthatches and juncos are only a few of the many mountain-dwelling birds.

Perhaps the most infuriating of all mountain fauna is the mosquito. As summer begins, clouds of this little beast may appear. The bite of the deerfly and horsefly may be more painful, and wood tick may be more feared, but the whine of the mosquito can drive humans and other animals mad. Luckily by mid-summer the woods are usually safe to enter.

All the animal inhabitants of the mountains require water, a commodity that is abundant in most of Montana's high country. Hundreds of cold, deep alpine lakes give rise to innumerable streams and rivers. Most of the lakes support populations of fish, and anglers can test their skill against cutthroat, rainbow, brook and brown trout in the lakes and cascading streams of the mountains.

Of all the resources found in the mountains of Montana, wildlife habitat and its corresponding and highly dependent animal populations may yet be the most valuable of all. They require and merit the most careful stewardship by the people of Montana and the nation.

From Lewis and Clark, to the legendary mountain men, to the Indian writings and wisdom, western history is alive with references to the grizzly bear. No historian could imagine the West without its great bear.

Soon, however, historians may be writing the final chapter of the reign of the grizzly bear. Since Lewis and Clark ventured into what is now Montana and met the great "white" bear, mountain range after mountain range has been deprived of its dominant species, the king of the wilderness, the grizzly. In Montana, only Yellowstone National Park, Glacier National Park, their surrounding wildlands and a few of the wildest ranges now have grizzlies.

Although grizzlies occasionally wander into populated areas, the bear depends for its existence on roadless areas — not because such areas provide the best habitat, but because only here can the bear find refuge from humankind. Even today, the grizzly could probably survive in the breaks and sagebrush flats of eastern Montana, but man won't allow this. We will only allow the grizzly to exist in the remote mountain cirques of western Montana.

Montana probably has more grizzlies than any state excluding Alaska. And while the grizzly still ranges over several million acres of western Montana, its numbers have now dwindled to a few hundred.

The decline of the grizzly has followed closely the decline of the Great American Wilderness. The grizzly's prairie domain, perhaps the best habitat for the great bear, went first. Then the easternmost mountain ranges became bearless. Before long, only the roadless mountains of western Montana had retained enough of their wild character to support the grizzly. Now, the last islands of refuge for the big bear are under siege. The advance of civilization, particularly energy and mining development, may soon mean the end of the grizzly in Montana.

"One thing we have learned about the grizzly bear is that wilderness is essential," notes bear expert Dr. John Craighead. "Wherever you bring people into

Grizzly bear. (MICHAEL FRANCIS)

close proximity to the grizzly, the grizzly suffers one way or another. This is not a difficult species to eliminate."

Why should we worry about the grizzly? Why do we need them at all? Because, as biologists tell us, losing one more species out of an intricate chain of life creates less diversity and less stability.

That is, however, merely a biological truism — everyone who has camped, hiked, hunted or otherwise enjoyed grizzly country knows that these majestic mountains won't be nearly as majestic without the grizzly. They will seem smaller and tamer, and the allure of wild, untrammeled nature will be gone forever.

CHAPTER FOUR

ISOLATED RANGES OF SOUTHWEST MONTANA

Flint Creek, Garnet, Sapphire, Anaconda, Pioneer, Highland, Tobacco Root, Ruby and Snowcrest Ranges

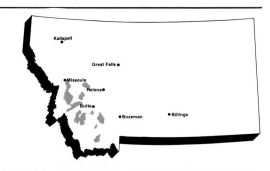

by Rick Reese

In the southwest corner of Montana, in an area lying south of Missoula and between the Bitterroot and Beaverhead ranges on the extreme western border of Montana and the Madison-Gallatin area on the east, are situated nine clearly definable mountain clusters. Varying from small uplifts of only a few dozen square miles to relatively large, high ranges, these isolated mountains form a chain of alpine and sub-alpine oases roughly in the shape of a large "S." The top of the "S" begins in the Flint Creek range west of Deer Lodge, thence north through the Garnet Range and west into the Sapphire Mountains before swinging southeast to the Anaconda Mountains then down to the Pioneer Mountains. From the Pioneers the "S" swings slightly northeast to the Highland Mountains then southeast to the Tobacco Root Mountains before dropping south through the Ruby and Snowcrest ranges.

The Flint Creek Range provides a continuous mountain barrier separating the Deer Lodge Valley on the east from the Philipsburg Valley on the west. The peaks here are generally lower and more gently shaped than other ranges in southwestern Montana. Most of the summits are in the 8,000 to 9,000-foot range, but imposing Mt. Powell, just west of Deer Lodge, reaches well over 10,000 feet. The topography of the Flint Creek Range was affected heavily by glaciation. All the lakes and cirques are glacier-formed and glacial moraines extend right down to the floor of the Deer Lodge Valley.

Some of the major drainages of the Flint Creek Range are roaded, but enough wild country remains to encompass a nearly 60,000-acre wilderness proposal for the area. Discerning recreationists can still find a great deal of untrammeled high country here.

North of the Flint Creeks beyond Interstate 90, the Clark Fork River follows a giant fault which separates the Garnet Range from the mountains to the south. Best known for its early-day mining camps, the Garnet Range stretches 65 miles along its northwest-southeast axis, a mass of forested mountains with an extensive system of logging roads and clear cuts. The sedimentary and young volcanic rocks of the range contain many contact zones along which high mineralization occurs, and mining activity, past and present, is evident. The ghost towns of Coloma and Garnet, former gold and silver camps, are in the heart

Opposite page: The peaks of the Flint Creek Range rise to more than 10,000 feet and harbor more than two dozen alpine lakes. (CHARLES KAY)
Above: Autumn along Rock Creek in the Sapphire Mountains southeast of Missoula. (RON GLOVAN)

27

Left: Gorge Lake in the lofty East Pioneer Mountains. (RON GLOVAN)
Bottom: A winter day near Grasshopper Creek in the gently rolling forests of the West Pioneers. (GEORGE WUERTHNER)
Right: Peaks of the Anaconda Range rise above a sea of lupine. (RON GLOVAN)
Far right: Electric Peak in the Anaconda-Pintler Wilderness of southwest Montana. (RON GLOVAN)

of the mountains. Most of the peaks here are in the 6,000 to 7,000-foot range, but a cluster of higher peaks north of Gold Creek in the eastern part of the range reach well over 7,000 feet.

To the south and east most of the rolling 8,000-foot hills of the Sapphire Range remain wild — 98,000 acres have been designated by Congress as a wilderness study area and an additional 100,000 acres proposed as the Stony Mountain Wilderness. Excellent "spruce-moose" habitat and elk summer range are found in the Sapphires along with very high watershed values. These mountains give rise to the pure tributaries of Rock Creek on the east and the Bitterroot River on the west.

The most prominent ranges in this "S" cluster are the Anacondas, the Pioneers and the Tobacco Roots. The Anaconda Range lies south and west of the smelter city of Anaconda and stretches about 40 miles directly along the Continental Divide. The heart of the range is encompassed in the 159,000-acre Anaconda-Pintler Wilderness which includes

portions of four counties and three national forests. Topography and vegetation within the range are diverse, from the low willow flats along the Bitterroot River on the west to the pocket of 9,000 and 10,000-foot peaks in the center of the range where evidence of past glaciation abounds. Here, within a few miles one can travel through a variety of life zones from heavy varied forest cover, where more than a dozen coniferous species can be identified, to austere peaks where only the hardiest primitive lichens and mosses exist. A partial listing of the more than two dozen native mammals found in the Anaconda-Pintler Wilderness includes elk, deer, mountain goat, beaver, flying squirrel, wolverine, lynx, badger and mountain lion. The area is also host to several dozen species of birds including 13 varieties of raptors.

The Big Hole Valley to the southeast of the Anaconda Range separates it from the Pioneer Mountains. The Pioneers are surrounded on three sides by the Big Hole River and on the south by Highway 278. The town of Dillon is situated just off

the southeast corner of the range. The Pioneer Mountains are split into two sub-ranges by the Wise River and a dirt road which crosses longitudinally through the entire range from the town of Wise River on the north to Polaris on the south. The wild and largely unroaded condition of the West Pioneers resulted in their designation as a wilderness study area; the East Pioneers have been recommended for wilderness designation. Even though the Forest Service has recommended against wilderness in the West Pioneers, high wilderness values abound here. A stand of some of the world's oldest known lodgepole pine — more than 500 years old — lives in these mountains, and the easternmost stand of alpine larch in the world also exists here. Some of these trees are more than 700 years old. Lakes of the West Pioneers are some of the few in the state that harbor the rare arctic grayling fish.

The East Pioneers are a long, narrow stretch of high alpine peaks surrounded by lower forested foothills and one of only half a dozen ranges in Montana with

11,000-foot peaks. The West Pioneers, by contrast, are lower, gentler, and more rounded than their eastern neighbors but no less wild. Together the more than half a million acres in the Pioneer Mountains harbor 86 lakes, large expanses of critical elk winter range and the headwaters of some of the world's finest fishing streams. The area has become a popular site for winter sports in recent years with heavy use by cross-country and downhill skiers as well as snowmobilers.

The Beaverhead Valley formed by the Beaverhead, Big Hole and Ruby Rivers, lies to the east of the Pioneers. The valley was named after Beaverhead Rock, a landmark recognized by Sacajawea as she guided Lewis and Clark up the headwaters of the Missouri River 180 years ago. On the opposite side of the valley from the Pioneers and about 35 miles distant rise the Tobacco Root Mountains. Considerably smaller in extent than either the Anaconda Range or the Pioneers, the Tobacco Roots are scarcely 30 miles long and less than 10 miles wide

Above: An alpine lake embellishes a high cirque in the Tobacco Root Mountains south of Whitehall. (RICK GRAETZ)
Right: The Tobacco Root Mountains loom above a ranch near Harrison, Montana. (GEORGE WUERTHNER)

in places. They are encompassed by the Jefferson River and its headwaters on the west and north, by the Madison Valley on the east, and by a line of low hills near Virginia City on the south. This is a highly mineralized area and has been the site of considerable mining exploration and development, especially during the long-past boom years of Alder and Virginia City. The Forest Service regarded the wilderness character of the Tobacco Roots highly enough to designate 40,000 acres of the range as a "roadless further planning area," but extensive mining claims and off-road vehicle use make wilderness designation unlikely. The miners' roads and trails provide access to some of the deepest recesses of the range but the high country, remains nearly pristine. Twenty-six peaks above 10,000 feet, one of the densest concentrations of high peaks in Montana, form a barrier to all but foot travelers.

On the far northern edge of the Beaverhead Valley along the Continental Divide lies a small cluster of peaks known as the Highland Mountains. The Highlands, situated just south of the city of Butte, are composed primarily of steep, forested slopes, with a few peaks in the area that exceed 10,000 feet. Dirt roads cover much of the north and central portion of the Highlands, but a relatively large area around Table Mountain is nearly devoid of the imprint of human activity.

About 35 miles south across the Beaverhead Valley rises the small, isolated Ruby Range, dominated by a north-south ridge line reaching more than 9,000 feet at the summit of Ruby Mountain. While most of the land in the Ruby Mountains is in public ownership, none is national forest. Instead, the land is administered by the Bureau of Land Management (BLM), which has recommended a portion of the area for wilderness status.

Twenty-five miles south and slightly east of the Ruby's, the Snowcrest range rises 10,581 feet to the summit of Sunset Peak. There are 60,000 acres of BLM and national forest wildland in the Snowcrest (considered by some to be a subsidiary range of the Gravelly Range), but the area is one of the least-known wild areas in Montana. Several 10,000-foot peaks ascend into this island of beauty among the valleys of southwestern Montana and the scenic Snowcrest Trail winds its way for nearly twenty miles along the high ridges of the range.

Above: A fog-shrouded forest near the Continental Divide in the Anaconda Range. (RON GLOVAN)
Left top: Red Mountain in the Highland Mountain Range. (PAT CAFFREY)
Bottom: The little-known Snowcrest Range rises grasslands of southwestern Montana to more than 10,000 feet. (LARRY LEWIS)

CHAPTER FIVE

THE BROAD VALLEY RANGES:

Bridger, Crazy, Big Belt, Little Belt, Elkhorn, Castle and Highwood Mountains

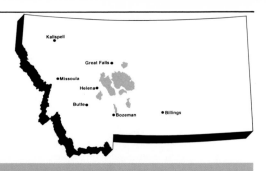

by Rick Reese

Left: Morning light warms the high peaks of the Crazy Mountains. (TIM CHURCH)
Right: Knife-edge ridges sweep upward in graceful arcs to the highest summits of the Crazy Mountains. (RICK GRAETZ)

In west-central Montana four major mountain ranges and three lesser ones are encompassed within a giant imaginary circle whose circumference is roughly defined by Great Falls, Helena, Bozeman and Lewistown. Across the 13,000 square miles of this expanse rise the Bridger Range, the Crazy Mountains, the Big Belt Mountains, the Little Belt Mountains, and the smaller Highwood, Castle, Big Snowy and Elkhorn Mountains.

Near the bottom of this imaginary circle the valley of the Shields River separates the Bridger and the Crazy Mountains, the two most impressive ranges among this group. The Crazies rise abruptly from the Shields River on the west and the vast plains on the east, to high, extremely rugged peaks and ridges. Twenty-three peaks here are above 10,000 feet — half of them unnamed. Crazy Peak, the highest point in the range, rises to well over 11,000 feet. The stark shapes of the Crazies evidence the heavy imprint of extensive glaciation which has gouged the peaks in several directions simultaneously.

The Crazy Mountains are volcanic in origin. Some

25 square miles of the highest portion are bare igneous rock intruded between uplifted beds of sediment. These formations titillate the hopes of geologists searching for beds of trapped gas. The controversy over resource development is complicated here by the same checkerboard land ownership present in neighboring ranges to the southwest. Nineteenth century railroad land grants, now mostly passed on to other parties, make coherent resource management difficult. Several efforts at legal protection for the remaining wild areas of the Crazy Mountains have failed in the past, but conservationists have once again proposed wilderness designation for 90,000 acres of the Crazies. For the moment, however, the Crazy Mountains remain the most spectacular alpine range in Montana without wilderness protection.

West of the Crazies across the Shields Valley, the crest of the Bridger Range reaches nearly 10,000 feet. Unlike the Crazy Mountains, the Bridgers are uplifted fault blocks, and sedimentary rocks dominate here. The fertile Gallatin Valley borders the Bridgers on the

Crazy Mountains from the west. The source for the name of these peaks is unclear. One legend says a woman, driven crazy when Indians slaughtered her family, retreated to the mountains to haunt the Indians Geologists think the name refers to the contorted geological formations in these peaks. (SANDRA CAHILL)

southwest, and the city of Bozeman lies just to the south. The Bridgers also have been affected dramatically by glaciation, and though glaciers no longer carve these peaks, an abundant snowfall makes the Bridger Bowl Ski Area one of the best deep powder skiing areas in the country.

A few miles north and slightly west of the Bridgers the southern end of the Big Belt Mountains begins. From a point east of Townsend, the Big Belts parallel the Missouri River in a southeast-northwest line for nearly 50 miles before dwindling about 20 miles northeast of Helena. Portions of the Big Belts are covered by large areas of precipitous limestone canyons whose intricate rock formations remind the visitor of the canyonlands of the southwestern United States. Few peaks reach above timberline in the Big Belts but near the southern end of the range the Mt. Baldy glacial cirque soars to 9,472 feet. A proposed 16,000-acre wilderness in this region has received wide-spread support in recent years.

In the mid-nineteenth century gold mines boomed in the canyons of the Big Belts but today the area

yields prized recreational opportunities, valuable water, timber and grazing. In the north end of the range the relatively small, compact Gates of the Mountains Wilderness affords protection for about 29,000 acres of scenic Missouri River back country. Here, in 1805, Lewis and Clark first entered the Rocky Mountains on their journey up the Missouri. As they approached the enormous limestone cliffs of the Big Belts, Capt. Lewis feared the river would not lead them through the barrier. But as they drew closer he could see the river pass through a narrow canyon which he appropriately named "Gates of the Mountains."

Northeast of the Big Belts, across the Smith River Valley, the Little Belt Mountains appear. Similar in topography to the Big Belts but somewhat greater in extent, the Little Belts extend from a point about 20 miles south of Great Falls for some 65 miles southeast to the Judith Basin. U.S. 89 crosses the center of the range at 7,393-foot King's Hill. As in the neighboring Big Belts, elevations are generally under 9,000 feet and forest cover extends across most of the range. Watershed is perhaps the single most important resource in the Little Belts, where high-quality Missouri River tributaries originate. The Smith River flows through a beautiful limestone canyon along the west side of the Little Belts, providing floaters the most popular overnight river trip in Montana. Conservationists have proposed that 90,000 acres of this area be set aside as the Tenderfoot-Deep Creek Wilderness.

The Little Belts provide superb, diverse wildlife habitat, and elk transplants of decades ago have been extremely successful. Recreational opportunities in the area abound, and timber production and grazing provide valuable resources as well. Commercial mining ended shortly after World War II, but considerable mineral potential remains. At Yogo Gulch near the eastern edge of the range, sapphires

The foothills of the Big Belts slope off to Canyon Ferry Reservoir northeast of Helena. (BRUCE SELYEM)
At right: Limestone cliffs of the Big Belt Mountains in the Gates of the Mountains area north of Helena. (JOHN REDDY)

for the crown jewels of England were mined. Here also is the nearly pristine Middle Fork of the Judith River, an area which has been dropped from wilderness consideration by the Forest Service. Conservationists still hope that about 80,000 acres here will ultimately be designated as wilderness.

This is picturesque country of deep, narrow limestone canyons, open meadows and forests. It includes a few tributary streams which still harbor threatened populations of pure cutthroat trout. Small wonder this country was a favorite of Charlie Russell, who wrote about it, painted it and visited it frequently.

Immediately north of the Little Belts the small, isolated Highwood Mountains rise, a remnant of long-since eroded volcanoes. Nearly half of the Highwoods are grasslands and the highest points reach less than 8,000 feet. Geologists are fascinated

by the unusual laccoliths and dikes (volcanic intrusions) in the Highwoods, and city dwellers from nearby Great Falls pursue a variety of recreational activities here.

On the other side of the Little Belts emerges yet another small range, the Castle Mountains. The Castles were formed by a granite intrusion and they are geologically much different from the Little Belts. Large silver mines flourished in the Castles until the mid-1890s, but today logging and livestock production are the predominant economic activities.

Immediately southeast of the capital city of Helena lie the Elkhorn Mountains. A relatively small range by Montana standards, the Elkhorns are mostly undeveloped and contain large roadless portions. Most of the range lies below timberline and is characterized by large open parks interspersed with rock outcroppings and coniferous forests. In the southern end of the range, Elkhorn and Crow Peaks reach elevations of well above 9,000 feet.

In recent years political controversy has swirled around the Elkhorn Mountains as competing resource values have been argued. Due to their proximity to Helena, these mountains receive considerable recreational use, mostly in the form of hiking, hunting, camping and cross-country skiing. The wildlife values of the Elkhorns have been formally recognized recently through an arrangement in which the forest service has agreed to manage the entire 160,000-acre area as a "special wildlife management unit." Under the provisions of this agreement, wildlife will be the top resource priority in the Elkhorns. The prototype agreement marks the first time that the needs of wildlife have been given priority over competing resource values on a large tract of national forest.

Left: Bear Prairie in the Gates of the Mountains Wilderness. (RICK GRAETZ)
Above: Crow Creek Falls in the Elkhorn Mountains. Recently this lovely falls was badly defaced by a gold-mining operation. (BILL CUNNINGHAM)

37

CHAPTER SIX

THE FORESTED RANGES OF NORTHWEST MONTANA

Cabinet, Purcell, Salish and Whitefish Mountains

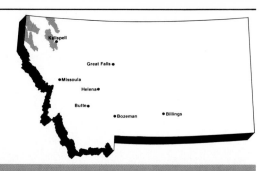

by Rick Reese

Sunlit ridges of the Cabinet Mountains stand above the Kootenai River of northwest Montana. (LANCE SCHELVAN)

The Cabinet Mountains are the dominant range of northwestern Montana. They extend about 80 miles along a northwest-southeast axis and are bounded by the Idaho state line on the west, the Clark Fork River and Highway 200 on the south, the Thompson River on the east, and the Kootenai River and Highway 2 on the north.

The Cabinets can be divided into southeast, central, and northwest sub-sections. These three areas are set apart by the peaks of the Cabinet Mountains Wilderness Area which form the dominant central portion of the range. These peaks seem almost out of place — as if they belonged to an altogether different range. They form a 35-mile-long wilderness of nearly 100,000 acres of jagged peaks, high lake basins, and open country affording spectacular alpine views. The summits are relatively low, but surrounding elevations are the lowest in Montana, and the resultant relief creates impressive mountains. The highest point in the range is 8,712-foot Snowshoe Peak, and the Cabinets themselves are the highest mountains between Glacier National Park on the east and the Cascade range of Washington State on the west. As such, they form one of the first major mountain barriers to eastward-flowing Pacific storms which drop up to 100 inches of precipitation here each year.

The canyons forming the northern flank of the mountains toward Libby are long and U-shaped, and distinct primary ridges emanate from the divide here. On the south, canyons are steep and glacier-carved but more truncated than those on the north. An excellent trail system leads into the high peaks from road heads on all sides of the range and provides good access to the sub-alpine terrain of the Cabinet Mountains Wilderness Area.

The mountains of the southeast portion are lower and less rugged than the wilderness summits. Several peaks here are more than 7,000 feet high including 7,429-foot Mt. Headley which dominates a region of peaks and lakes in an unroaded area above the town of Thompson Falls. Forty thousand acres of this area have been proposed as a Cabinet Lake Country Wilderness. The country here is not as dramatically rugged as the Cabinet Mountains Wilderness Area, but it is dotted with two dozen mountain lakes. Logging is a major activity in the non-wilderness

Left: Bald Eagle Peak in the Cabinet Mountains Wilderness. (LANCE SCHELVAN) *Below: The stark imprint of glacial carving is readily apparent in the deep canyons of the Cabinet Mountains.* (LANCE SCHELVAN)

"A" Peak (8,634 feet) and Snowshoe Peak (8,712 feet) rise above the forests of the Cabinet Mountains Wilderness Area. (RICK GRAETZ)

sections of the Cabinet Range, and much of the area has been roaded and clearcut. In areas where logging has not occurred, thick forests extend all the way to the ridgetops.

The Bull River Valley separates the peaks of the Cabinet Mountains Wilderness Area from the rest of the range to the northwest. The peaks of the northwest are the lowest in the range and reach elevations of only about 6,500 feet. As in the southeast portion of the range, logging and its associated road system are very evident. Nonetheless, 75,000 acres of this area in the proposed Scotchman Peaks Wilderness are pristine wildland and superb habitat for a variety of species including the severely endangered Cabinet grizzly population. Highway 56 leads to Spar Lake and a Forest Service recreation area

as well as to Bull Lake and the Ross Creek Giant Cedars, all popular features in the northwest Cabinets. From here the range slopes to the north to 1,802 feet above sea level, the lowest point in Montana, where the Kootenai River leaves Montana just west of Troy.

The jumble of mountains lying north of Libby and Troy in the extreme northwestern corner of Montana are the Purcells. They are bordered on the north by the Canadian border, on the east by the long, slender form of Lake Koocanusa, on the south by the Kootenai River, and on the west by Idaho.

Lake Koocanusa, the 35-mile-long body of water impounded behind Libby Dam, fills the former Kootenai River Valley. The lake's name was derived

by combining the words "Kootenai," "Canada," and "U.S.A."

As elsewhere in northwestern Montana, elevations here are relatively low. The highest mountains of the Purcells are found in and around the Northwest Peaks Scenic Area, but even here no peak attains 8,000 feet. Almost all the ridge lines and mountain tops are forest-covered, larch being the dominant species. Logging is the primary economic activity of northwestern Montana and its effect on the Purcells, a prime timber harvest region, is readily apparent.

There are several scenic roadless areas in the Purcell Range. The Northwest Peaks Scenic Area has been set aside as an area protected from logging and it contains several lake basins and superb mountain

Above: Upper Geiger Lake in the Cabinet Mountains Wilderness. (PAT O'HARA)
Right: Giant cedar trees and detail of cedar root system in the Ross Creek area of the Bull River Valley. Because of abundant moisture, this area of Montana resembles forests of the Pacific Northwest. (LANCE SCHELVAN PHOTOS)

Glacier lilies herald the coming of summer to the meadows of the Purcell Range. (LANCE SCHELVAN)

scenery. The areas around Mt. Robinson and Mt. Henry are also unroaded. Mt. Henry, a former wilderness study area, has now been dropped from wilderness consideration and is scheduled for logging.

The high country visible along the west shore of Flathead Lake and extending along the west side of Highway 93 from Kalispell through Whitefish and up to Eureka is known as the Salish Mountains. From its terminus on the south near the Thompson River and Buffalo Bill Divide, the high country of the Salish stretches north for nearly 100 miles almost to the Canadian border. Here in the northwestern part of the range east of Lake Koocanusa are found the only roadless portions in these mountains. The mountain tops in the northern end of the range are forest-covered and the highest points are all under 7,000 feet. Farther south the summits are lower still and

taper off to scattered hills devoid of timber.

Several large lakes in the northern Salish including Thompson, McGregor, Ashley, Little Bitterroot, Hubbard, and Tally Lakes, are perhaps the most dominant feature of the Salish country.

The Whitefish Range, north of the resort community of Whitefish, extends for more than 50 miles from Columbia Falls to the Canadian border along the western edge of Glacier National Park. When compared to the towering summits of Glacier to the east, the peaks of the Whitefish seem to pale. From the low valleys to the west it is a distinct and prominent mountain massif.

The peaks here are mostly in the 7,000-foot range with the highest point, Nasukoin Mountain, rising to 8,095 feet. Low valleys of less than 3,000 feet on the west, however, result in significant relief and give the Whitefish an impressive elevation differential. For

the most part the range is forested to the tops of the peaks and ridges, and a large part of it has been roaded and logged.

A major attraction of the northern Whitefish Range is the Ten Lakes Scenic Area, an unroaded region which was explored and written about by the famous naturalist Ernest Thompson Seton, founder of the Boy Scouts of America. Seton's popular short story "Krag, The Kootenay Ram" takes place here, and his writing has influenced the naming of three local peaks: Krag, Krinklehorn, and Mt. Thompson Seton.

Three proposed wilderness areas near the Canadian border (collectively called North Fork Wildlands) encompass 60,000 acres in the northern Whitefish. This is an area of extraordinary wildlife attributes where four endangered species, the Rocky Mountain gray wolf, bald eagle, grizzly bear, and an occasional mountain caribou find their homes. Here

in the northern part of the range is a cluster of beautiful peaks interspersed with larch-covered lake basins. Green Mountain (7,830 feet) is the highest peak in the area. A trail system, best reached from dirt roads south of Eureka, provides good access. A long logging road from Trail Creek on the North Fork of the Flathead River along the eastern edge of the range winds its way across the mountains to a trailhead which also leads into the Ten Lakes area.

No major waterways are born in these mountains. Waters of the eastern slopes flow into the North Fork of the Flathead, while the western slopes drain to the Stillwater and on to the Flathead. A portion of the extreme northwestern slope flows to the Kootenai River. Since the Whitefish Range and the other ranges of northwestern Montana lie west of the Continental Divide, all the waters arising here flow ultimately to the Pacific Ocean.

Left: The Clark Fork River near Thompson Falls. (CHARLES KAY)
Above: The Ten Lakes Scenic Area in the Whitefish Range. (JAN MACK)

CHAPTER SEVEN

RANGES OF THE WESTERN BOUNDARY

Bitterroot, Beaverhead, and Centennial Mountains

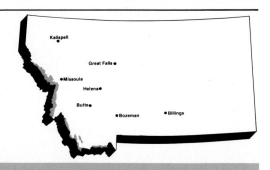

by Rick Reese

Trapper Peak (10,157 feet) and Trapper Creek Canyon in the Bitterroot Range southwest of Darby. Trapper Creek Canyon typifies the many U-shaped glacial canyons on the west side of the Bitterroot. This particular area of the range is known for its granite spires and rugged terrain. (MARK LAGERSTROM)
At right: Big Creek Lake in the Bitterroot Range. (GEORGE WUERTHNER)

The Bitterroot Range is the longest and one of most rugged of Montana's mountain chains. From Lookout Pass in the northwest to Raynolds Pass on the south, only three paved roads cross the range along its entire 470-mile length. The Bitterroots drain an enormous area with streams flowing to both sides of the Continental Divide and eventually emptying into both the Pacific Ocean and the Gulf of Mexico.

The Bitterroots can be divided into two major subranges: the Bitterroot proper, and the Beaverhead. These subranges can be further divided into several distinct groups of mountains. The northern section of the Bitterroot stretches from Lookout Pass to Lolo Pass and is composed of steep, heavily forested hills with few truly alpine peaks. This portion of the Bitterroots is one of the wettest areas in the state with well over 100 inches of precipitation recorded annually along some ridgetops. This moisture nurtures dense forests which have been extensively logged since the turn of the century. A dry summer in 1910 gave rise to the "Great Burn" of August 20-22 in which 3 million acres of northwestern Montana forest land was on fire. In the wake of that fire, extensive areas of subalpine meadow and brush-filled valleys grew up among the silver skeletons of long-dead trees. Some valleys which escaped the fire now harbor huge stands of western red cedar, hemlock, and lodgepole pine.

Some 90,000 acres of the Bitterroots between Hoodoo and Lolo passes may ultimately be protected as the proposed Great Burn Wilderness. In conjunction with nearly 250,000 acres of adjacent wild country in Idaho, the Great Burn is one of the largest chunks of unprotected wildland in the Northern Rockies. The Stateline Trail runs for more than fifty miles from Eagle Cliff on the north through several roadless subalpine basins (known as the "String of Pearls") and on south through the Great Burn proposed wilderness. This magnificent footpath follows the crest of the Bitterroot though broad rolling hills and along knife-edge ridges past dozens of subalpine lakes. Although little-known today by back-country travellers, this trail is surely one of the classic mountain hikes in Montana.

The southern section of the Bitterroot, which encompasses the Selway-Bitterroot Wilderness Area, holds some of the most convoluted mountain terrain

Along Montana's western boundary, the "Great Burn" — site of an enormous wildfire early in this century — straddles the Continental Divide. (GEORGE WUERTHNER)

in all of Montana; jagged granite pinnacles, precipitous walls, and canyons of classic glacial shape dominate the landscape. Summits here generally vary from 9,000 to 10,000 feet in elevation and Trapper Peak, a splendid crag southwest of Darby, is the highest point in the range. From Trapper Peak south the mountains are lower and more heavily forested. At Lost Trail Pass (named by Lewis and Clark when they lost their way here), the Bitterroot crest joins the Continental Divide as it veers in from the northeast out of the Anaconda-Pintler Wilderness Area. The Beaverhead Mountains begin here.

The Beaverhead range can be divided into the West Big Hole Mountains (between Lost Trail and Lemhi Pass), the Italian Peaks (from Mt. Baldy to Lemhi Pass), the Lima Peaks (sometimes referred to as the Red Conglomerate or Garfield Peaks and extending from Medicine Lodge Pass to Monida Pass), and the Centennial Range (which extends from Monida Pass east to Raynolds Pass and on into Henry's Lake, Idaho).

The Beaverhead Mountains are narrower than their northern neighbors. The Big Hole Valley and its side canyons bound the mountains on the east and north, and the Salmon and Lemhi River valleys of Idaho border them on the west. The peaks are less rugged than those in the Selway-Bitterroot Wilderness but are generally higher and more massive. Many exceed 10,000 feet including Eighteenmile Peak (11,141 feet), the highest in the range, and 10,998-foot Italian Peak. Small offshoots of the Beaverhead Mountains extend north of the Continental Divide near Lima into the Lima Peaks and the Tendoy Mountains. This is high, open country where valley bottoms nurture some of Montana's finest aspen stands.

Most of the Beaverhead Range is only five to ten miles wide, but the West Big Hole Mountains are more massive. They rise abruptly and spectacularly from the town of Salmon, Idaho on their western edge. On the Montana side of the Continental Divide the West Big Holes present a series of long, U-shaped glacial canyons which lead gradually to the floor of the Big Hole Valley. It is these canyons and peaks that have impressed wildland advocates enough to call for an 86,000-acre wilderness area here.

Top: El Capitan pierces the sky in western Montana's Bitterroot Range. (DICK BEHAN)
Bottom: The remote Italian peaks occupy the southernmost point of Montana. (ED MADEJ)

The Continental Divide winds its way along the high ridges of the Garfield Peaks in the Beaverhead Range. (GEORGE WUERTHNER)

The southern flank of Eighteenmile Peak in the Beaverhead Range, the highest point along a thousand-mile stretch of the Continental Divide. (RICK GRAETZ)

The crest of Garfield Peak defines the boundary between Montana and Idaho. (GEORGE WUERTHNER)

Between the West Big Hole Mountains and the Italian Peaks, Elk Mountain (10,200 feet) lies astride the Continental Divide. It is the highest peak on the Continental Divide National Scenic Trail in Montana. Farther south in the Italian Peaks, Eighteenmile Peak (11,141 feet) is the highest point on the Continental Divide between Banff National Park in Canada and the Washakie Wilderness in Wyoming. Nearby Scott Peak (11,393 feet), whose summit lies one mile into Idaho, is the highest peak in the entire 470-mile length of the Bitterroot Range. The high mountains surrounding Scott Peak are at the heart of the nearly 100,000-acre proposed Italian Peaks Wilderness. Within the proposed wilderness itself is Italian Peak, the most southerly point in the state of Montana.

From here the mountains drop to Monida Pass and to Interstate 15 where they turn almost directly west and run for some 40 miles along the Montana-Idaho border. This is the Centennial Range. It borders the southern side of the remote Centennial Valley, home of the fabulous Red Rocks National Wildlife Refuge. The refuge, famous for the rare trumpeter swan and a vast array of waterfowl, features several large lakes in a beautiful mountain valley. The highest peaks in the Centennials approach 10,000 feet and the little-visited high country here is under active consideration as a possible wilderness area. The eastern end of the Centennials forms the terminus of the greater Bitterroot Range as it drops off to Henry's Lake just a few miles west of Yellowstone National Park.

Below: A mountain stream drops through a high canyon in the Centennial Mountains. (GEORGE WUERTHNER)
Right: Autumn aspen in the Centennial Valley. (RICK GRAETZ)
Right bottom: The Centennial Valley of southwestern Montana and the Centennial Range near Red Rock Lakes National Wildlife Refuge. (GEORGE WUERTHNER)

(U.S. FOREST SERVICE PHOTOS)

"WHITE DEATH." An avalanche carries thousands of tons of snow down a mountainside, wreaking destruction in its path. Such slides can reach velocities of more than a hundred miles per hour and the air blasts that precede them can snap large trees. Enormous avalanches can occur on relatively low-angle slopes and are extremely unpredictable. They pose a severe hazard for climbers, skiers and snowmobilers throughout the winter and spring months. Danger is generally greatest during and after winter storms but at the cold temperatures, experienced in Montana, instability in the snow pack may last for days or even weeks. In these photos a large soft slab avalanche builds into an enormous cloud of high-speed destruction.

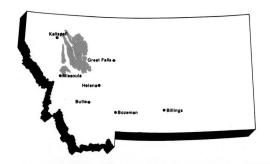

CHAPTER EIGHT

GREAT RANGES OF THE NORTHERN DIVIDE

Mountains of Bob Marshall, Great Bear, Scapegoat, Swan Range, Mission Mountain and Rattlesnake Wilderness Areas

by Rick Graetz and Rick Reese

Southward into Montana from the Canadian line and along the Continental Divide for 175 miles as the eagle flies, lies an area often called "The Crown Jewel of America." From north to south and east to west the region features magnificent mountains, high lakes, river canyons, large expanses of forest and some of the finest outdoor recreational opportunities in the nation. It also contains Glacier National Park, a large state game preserve, and five national wilderness areas. This is the epitome of wild mountain country.

From Glacier Park south the Bob Marshall, Great Bear and Scapegoat country is either legally designated or *de facto* mountain wilderness. The area is defined on the north by Glacier Park, on the west by the Swan Range and Swan Valley, on the south by the valley of the Blackfoot River, and on the east by the Rocky Mountain Front.

Physical access on the west is limited by the abruptness of the Swan Range, but in other areas roads lead easily to the wilderness boundary. Not a single road crosses the area, but one can drive the perimeter — a 380-mile journey.

This is the country of the contiguous million and a half acre Bob Marshall, Great Bear and Scapegoat Wilderness Areas and is home to almost every big game species found in North America, including the endangered grizzly bear. Bald and golden eagles soar from its precipitous canyon walls, and occasional wolves may still prowl here.

From its interior and high country are born two of Montana's blue ribbon trout streams: the South and Middle Forks of the Flathead River. Other major

Along the eastern edge of the Bob Marshall country the remarkable Rocky Mountain Front sweeps suddenly upward to 4,000 feet above the plains. (GEORGE WUERTHNER)

A winter day along the canyons and ridges of the Rocky Mountain Front. (RICK GRAETZ)

streams and rivers also emanate from the northern divide country: the Sun River, which drains the area east of the Continental Divide; the South Fork of the Two Medicine River flowing north toward Glacier Park; Birch Creek, flowing east from the divide to the prairie; Badger Creek, rising in the peaks of the Front Range and surging eastward; and the Dearborn River, headwatering along the east wall of Scapegoat Mountain and rushing southeast to the Missouri River. Peaks along the Rocky Mountain Front are generally in the 8,000 to 9,000-foot range with 9,392-foot Rocky Mountain Peak west of Choteau the highest.

This mountain country and its environs are steeped in the history of Indians and early-day mountain men. Its passes and river valleys served as passageways for Indians to the west in search of buffalo on the prairie beyond the mountain wall. Gateway Pass near the headwaters of the South Fork of Birch Creek and Lewis and Clark Pass miles to the south were favorite routes. Blackfeet warriors who controlled the lands bordering the peaks on the east would ambush other tribes returning across these passes from the plains. Indians also frequented Medicine Springs at the confluence of the North and South Forks of the Sun River just west of Gibson Lake. Throughout the area tepee rings and petroglyphs are evident as are travois tracks, still discernible today from travel along the Great North Trail which was used by these early inhabitants of North America. Atop Half Dome Crag west of Heart Butte, Indians sought visions from the Great Spirit.

The Rocky Mountain Front, with its great relief and towering limestone walls rising abruptly from the prairie, is the western-most range in this group of mountains. It is the best known of the wilderness ranges not only because of it geographic location but because of its popularity with recreationists and more recently because of sharp resource management controversies which have occurred there.

From the summits of the Rocky Mountain Front —
Castle Reef, Sawtooth Ridge, Old Man of the Hills, Ear Mountain and others —one can see for 100 miles or more. Access to trails leading to the interior of the range is possible via roads up both forks of the Teton River, Birch, Badger, Elk and Wood Creeks. From the Gibson country, the Sun river and Benchmark roads connect via a north-south road through Beaver and Little Willow Creek canyons.

The geology of the area is stunning. The Front is part of the Lewis Overthrust Belt where older rock formations slid across younger ones. The mountains here look like shuffled cards and slope to the west while dropping steeply on their eastern faces. This phenomenon can be readily observed along the road to Gibson Lake west of Augusta where the road cuts through four distinct ridges of the same formation.

The heavy floods of 1964 and 1975 ravaged many of the lower reaches of the Front Range canyons. Heavy June rains fell on a deep mountain snowpack, creeks and rivers were swollen beyond their banks, cutting huge swaths on their rush to the prairie. What

The Blackleaf Game Range along the Rocky Mountain Front is being eagerly eyed by energy developers. (CHARLES KAY)

Sawtooth Ridge, a prominent landmark on the Rocky Mountain Front west of Augusta. (KRISTI DuBOIS)

53

were once grassy meadows or forested banks are now sterile, boulder-strewn flats which bear a strong resemblance to the glacial streams of Alaska.

As elsewhere in the mountains of Montana, wildlife abounds along the Rocky Mountain Front. The State of Montana maintains the Sun River Game Preserve where a large elk herd flourishes. The largest bighorn sheep population in the United States finds a home along the Front. And only here does the grizzly bear, once a plains animal, still venture out to the swamp willow bottoms and aspen thickets of the intermountain flat lands.

To the west, the valleys of the Two Medicine, Sun and Dearborn Rivers separate the Rocky Mountain Front from the Continental Divide Range. The same type of geology exists in these mountains but with a few exceptions it is not as pronounced. One of those exceptions is the Chinese Wall and Wall Creek Cliffs, a 15-mile-long barrier which rises more than 1,000 feet above the meadows below its eastern face. Scapegoat Mountain (9,204 feet) to the south,

another massive limestone escarpment, is also a prominent feature of the Divide Range. Near the southern end of the wilderness just north of Rogers Pass, the mountains of the Divide Range and the Rocky Mountain Front come together and dwindle into lower foothills.

In the early 1980s energy companies announced plans to explore for natural gas in the Bob Marshall, Great Bear and Scapegoat Wilderness areas. Public opposition was so great that it sparked a nationwide movement to ban energy development in established wilderness areas. There is similar concern for the 900,000 acres of unprotected wildlands surrounding the Bob Marshall. Conservationists are now asking Congress to add a half million acres of wild country in the Swan Range, Monture Creek area, and especially the Rocky Mountain Front to the Bob Marshall wilderness in order to more fully protect the area's superb wildlife populations and spectacular outdoor recreation opportunities.

Along the Rocky Mountain Front east of the Bob Marshall wilderness the prospect of major invasions into the mountains in search of natural gas still threatens. It is not known if gas exists in large quantities under this area or if it would be economical to tap it. Similar formations in Alberta have contained natural gas. But even if gas does exist under the Rocky Mountain Front, estimates are that the total amount available could only provide the nation with a few months' supply. And though loss of the wilderness resource and its accompanying wildlife, watershed and recreation values may be a very high price to pay for a few months' supply of gas, the threat to the Front and the surrounding country remains strong as America intensifies the search for domestic gas to feed its insatiable appetite for energy.

To the west again, the Middle Fork of the Flathead River, Spotted Bear River, Dolly Varden Creek and many smaller streams separate the Continental Divide Range from a central range of mountains. The northern part of this central range, which parallels the

Left top: Beargrass thrives in an old burn beneath the imposing walls of Scapegoat Mountain in the Scapegoat Wilderness. From here the Continental Divide stretches north for 200 miles through the stupendous Bob Marshall country, into Glacier Park and Canada. (RICK GRAETZ)

Left bottom: Aerial view of the Chinese Wall in winter. This 13-mile-long limestone escarpment in the heart of the Bob Marshall Wilderness rises more than 1,000 feet in places. (RICK GRAETZ)

Below: The gentle west slope of the Chinese Wall stands above the White River in the Bob Marshall Wilderness. (RICK GRAETZ)

Bob Marshall, godfather of Montana's wild and famous Bob Marshall Wilderness Area, is a legend among conservationists.

In the early 1930s Marshall formulated the idea that an organization was needed to preserve America's rapidly-dwindling wilderness. In 1935 he and others formed The Wilderness Society and for years he provided its main financial support.

In 1933 Marshall became Director of Forestry for the Office of Indian Affairs, and in 1937 he was appointed chief of the Division of Recreation and Lands. He frequently called for public ownership of American forest lands.

Operating from Washington and afoot in the forests, he was a one-man political machine, campaigning everywhere for preservation and recognition of the inherent value of wilderness. He secured administrative orders and legislation that set aside millions of acres of unroaded forest in primitive areas and forest reserves. In 1937 Marshall was years ahead of his time when he wrote the following words in *Nature Magazine:*

"Wilderness skeptics in almost all arguments raise the question: 'Why should we set aside a vast area for the enjoyment of a few hundred people when roads would make that area available for half a million? Aren't we obligated to consider what will bring the greatest good to the greatest number?'

"The doctrine of the greatest good to the greatest number does not mean that this laudable relationship has to take place on every acre. If it did, we would be forced to change our metropolitan art galleries into metropolitan bowling alleys. Our state universities, which are used by a minor fraction of the population, would be converted into state circuses where hundreds could be exhilarated for every one person who may be either exhilarated or depressed now. The Library of Congress would become a national hot dog stand.

"Ridiculous as all of this sounds, it is no more ridiculous than the notion that every acre of land devoted to outdoor recreation should be administered in a way that will give the maximum volume of use ...

"Year after year, the United States becomes more and more mechanized. The life of one person after another has been saturated by machinery. Human beings require compensations, and it seems inevitable that as the machine age expands, the need for an escape will also expand."

Today, more than ever, America needs to heed Marshall's words.

Bob Marshall, left, with Ward Shepard of the U.S. Forest Service, in 1925. (WILDERNESS SOCIETY PHOTO)

Above: View into the Sun River country and Bob Marshall Wilderness from Headquarters Pass. (GEORGE WUERTHNER)
Right: Gateway Gorge, Bob Marshall Wilderness. (BILL CUNNINGHAM)

east shore of Hungry Horse Lake, is sometimes called the Flathead Range. Great Northern Mountain is a particularly pronounced peak here, while to the south along the crest of this range Silvertip Mountain graces the very heart of the most remote section of the wilderness. South of Schaefer Meadows and the Flathead Range is a twenty mile-long escarpment called the Trilobite Range. These very remote mountains are named for the abundance of trilobite fossils, a primitive crustacean-like animal more than 500 million years old. Still farther south beyond the Chinese Wall is yet another cluster of peaks known as the "Flathead Alps."

The western-most range of the northern divide group of peaks is the Swan Range. It rises abruptly from the floor of the Swan Valley east toward the Bob Marshall. Its splendid peaks stand apart from the Bob Marshall itself, separated by the intervening valleys of the Danaher River and the South Fork of the Flathead. Streams east of the Swan crest drain into these valleys, while water courses to the west fall into the

The peaks of the northern Swan Range form the backdrop for the community of Big Fork. (RICK GRAETZ)

57

Hikers pause along the crest of the Swan Range.
(RICK GRAETZ)

The Swan Range soars 5,000 feet above the beautiful Flathead and Swan Valleys. For an unbroken stretch of a hundred miles the high summits, hanging valleys and more than 70 lakes guard the western edge of the Bob Marshall Wilderness. (RICK GRAETZ)

Swan Valley. Southern slopes of the Swan Range feed the Blackfoot River.

The Swan Range stretches in an unbroken line for 100 miles from northwest of Ovando in the Blackfoot Valley to Badrock Canyon northeast of Kalispell. The crest of the range rarely falls below 6,500 feet. Most people view the Swan from their car windows as they drive the highway through the Swan Valley. The western Swan Front which faces the Swan Valley displays enormous vertical relief, rising from less than 4,000 feet at the Swan River to 9,356 feet at the summit of Holland Peak in a distance of less than five miles. This steep gradient makes access to the southern Swan difficult and guards its alpine secrets well. Three groups of peaks, Ptarmigan (9,083 feet), Holland (9,356 feet) and Swan (9,289 feet) rise above nine thousand feet and support active glacial

systems. Many of the largest glacial cirques are hidden on the eastern side of the range by trailless canyons while the western cirques are guarded by the steep, densely vegetated slopes of the Swan Front.

With its wet climate, sharp peaks, and small glaciers, the southern Swan resembles the Cascade Range of Washington state. Coniferous trees including ponderosa pine, larch, Douglas fir and lodgepole pine dominate the lower elevations while alpine fir, alpine larch and whitebark pine abound at higher levels. In season the country provides beautiful displays of wildflowers.

The northern Swan, north of Inspiration Pass, is lower and less rugged than its southern counterpart and is therefore more accessible to hikers and horsepackers. The popular Jewel Basin Hiking Area is

found here along with the beautiful Alpine Trail which follows the crest of the range for 40 miles. Conservationists have proposed 155,000 acres of the Swan Range for wilderness protection as an addition to the Bob Marshall.

The view to the west from the high ridges of the Swan Range out across the Swan Valley and into the Mission Range is one of the finest mountain panoramas in the northern Rockies. Rising to the west of the Swan Valley, the Missions form a 60-mile-long wall of rugged glaciated peaks which separate the Swan country from the Flathead and Mission Valleys still farther to the west. Most of the range lies within the Mission Mountains Wilderness Area and the Mission Mountain Tribal Wilderness of the Flathead Indian Tribe. The federally designated wilderness encompasses nearly 75,000 acres.

Mission Falls and the Garden Wall in the Mission Mountains near St. Ignatius, Montana. (RAY MILLER)

Clockwise from left above: The Mission Mountains from across the Flathead River. (GEORGE WUERTHNER)
McDonald Peak, at 9,820 feet, is the highest in the Missions. (CHARLES KAY) *Sunrise Glacier from Point St. Charles.* (DAVE SWANSON) *The town of St. Ignatius is dwarfed by the uplift of the Mission Mountains.* (JOHN KREMPEL)

The community of Missoula endures a late spring storm. The Rattlesnake Mountains are beyond. (TOM DIETRICH)

The dominant features of the Mission Range are the jagged peaks and the nearly 200 high lakes. The sedimentary rocks that make up the Missions lend themselves to rapid weathering and erosion and this, coupled with glaciation, has provided the Missions their stunning and rugged scenery. Several small glaciers are still active today.

The highest peaks and largest lakes are in the southern end of the range. Beautiful turquoise lakes fill glacial cirques and high valleys. McDonald Peak, the highest in the range, is 9,820 feet high. The Missions, however, appear to be much higher, especially when viewed from the Flathead or Mission Valleys on the west. The southern end of the range serves as habitat for the grizzly bear and elsewhere in the Missions most other big game species, including mountain goats and bighorn sheep, roam.

Much of the Missions is above timberline, but the lower slopes are covered with western larch, Douglas fir and spruce, while scattered stands of alpine larch and alpine fir prevail in higher meadows.

The western side of the Missions rises precipitously from low valleys, and very steep, rugged terrain makes access to the high country difficult. This beautiful western aspect of the range lies almost entirely within the Flathead Indian Reservation. Access to the high Missions is easiest from the east where numerous Forest Service roads extend to the wilderness boundary. Private alternating sections of railroad lands held by the Burlington Northern Company occur in a portion of this area, and logging operations are evident as one drives the back roads.

Most recreational use in the Mission Mountains is restricted by deep snows to a few short summer months and the autumn hunting season. For the remainder of the year steep open slopes pose a high avalanche hazard over much of the range.

The southern slopes of the Mission Mountains taper off to the Jocko River and Placid Creek. Beyond, the Rattlesnake Mountains, sometimes called the "Missoula Hills," rise into an expanse of high country before dropping steeply southward into the Missoula Valley. In 1980 Congress included over 60,000 acres of the Rattlesnake country in the Rattlesnake National Recreation and Wilderness Area. Many of the summits here are more than 7,000 feet high and in the northwestern part of the range near Stuart and Mosquito Peaks several reach nearly 8,000 feet. A trail system accessible from Missoula leads into this beautiful part of the wilderness.

CHAPTER NINE

THE MOUNTAINS OF GLACIER PARK

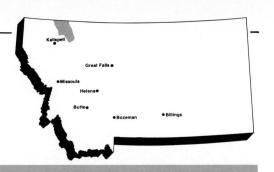

by Rick Graetz

Of all Montana's mountain ranges, those of Glacier National Park are perhaps the most famous. Bordered by Alberta and British Columbia on the north, Highway 2, Marias Pass and the Great Bear Wilderness on the south, the prairie lands of the Blackfeet Indian Reservation on the east, and the North Fork of the Flathead River and the Flathead Valley on the west, the mountains of Glacier may well be the most beautiful in all of Montana.

The glaciers of ice ages past did their finest work here, and the area serves as a living textbook on the forces of erosion and glaciation on sedimentary rocks. At one time glaciers filled most of the valleys to depths of more than 3,000 feet and spread far beyond the mountains. Even today some 60 shrunken glacial remnants remain high in the alpine cirques where a few still cover as much as several hundred acres each. The abrasion and plucking of these rivers of ice have left behind more than 200 lakes, countless waterfalls, towering rock walls thousands of feet high, and magnificent U-shaped valleys.

As the glacier spilled out of the high country, they cut very distinctive elongated lakes. Classic examples of such lakes are Two Medicine and St. Mary's on the east side of the park and McDonald and Kintla on the western flank.

Going-to-the-Sun Highway slashes the flanks of Garden Wall. (RAY MILLER)

Below: Glissading below Boulder Pass. (RICK GRAETZ)
Right: Alpine tarn in the morning sun. (JEFF GNASS)

The 50 Mountain region deep in the Glacier back country. (RICK GRAETZ)

Left: Mt. Oberlin framed by black cottonwood. (JEFF GNASS)
Right: St. Mary's Lake on the Park's east side. (GEORGE WUERTHNER)

The mountains of the Glacier country are part of the Lewis Overthrust Belt and can be viewed as an enormous slab of sedimentary rock that was dramatically displaced in the geologic past. Geologists estimate that entire ranges here were moved about 35 miles to the east. Older rocks virtually slid east over younger ones, leaving gigantic holes behind in the form of the Flathead and North Fork Valleys to the west. From the Flathead Valley north, the "Rocky Mountain Trench" extends far into northern Canada where the Canadian Rockies also left behind huge valleys as they were pushed eastward. The mountains here provide a geologic window into the distant past, and the peaks and canyons of Glacier offer a first-hand geology lesson which is exceeded by few places on earth.

Though rarely referred to as such, the peaks of Glacier actually are divided into two ranges: the Lewis Range to the east and the Livingston to the west. The Continental Divide runs north-south through the peaks, dividing the park roughly in two. At Logan Pass, Going-To-The-Sun-Highway crosses the Continental Divide and provides one of the most impressive auto tours in North America. The road is usually open from mid-June until late September when it is blocked by deep snows and drifts which may attain depths of 80 feet.

HIGHWAY

Fifty-one-mile-long Going-To-The-Sun-Highway is the only transmountain motor link between West Glacier on the west and St. Mary on the east. In the winter this road is impassable with snow drifts reaching heights of 60 feet. Usually open in early June, it offers tourists a dizzying ascent to the 6,644-foot summit of Logan Pass. During the years of planning and construction from 1916 to 1935, this project required blasting out cliff faces along the immense "Garden Wall" rock formation. The work season was limited to the fleeting summer months, making construction even more difficult. Gaining some 2,500 feet of elevation, Going-To-The-Sun-Highway offers extraordinary panoramas of waterfalls, red cedar forests, looming peaks and meadows of wildflowers. In testimony to the beauty of the road's vistas, Horace M. Albright, second director of the National Park Service, said: "Although Glacier will always be a trail park, the construction of this one highway to its inner wonders is meeting an obligation to the great mass of people who because of age, physical condition, or other reasons would never have an opportunity to enjoy close at hand this marvelous mountain park."

Going-to-the-Sun Highway, the only route across the Park for vehicles.
(JEFF GNASS PHOTOS)

With the exception of Going-To-The-Sun-Highway, the high country of Glacier Park is roadless. A paved road penetrates a short distance to the Many Glacier region on the east and a dirt road up the North Fork of the Flathead River parallels the western edge of the park. Elsewhere in Glacier you hike if you want to see the park.

The peaks in Glacier are not as high as in other Montana ranges, but the surrounding country is also lower and the net elevation differential from valley to peak makes the mountains seem higher than they are. Mt. Cleveland at 10,430 feet in the north end of the park is the highest mountain in Glacier. Its north face rises 6,700 feet in only four miles, making it the steepest vertical uplift in the Northern Rockies. From its summit one can see far into Waterton National Park, Glacier's Canadian sister park. Together these parks comprise a monument to international conservation efforts.

Other prominent peaks of the dozens which rise in Glacier are 9,380-foot Mt. St. Nicholas, a stark tower visible from Highway 2 on the southern end of the park; 9,157-foot Mt. Reynolds; 8,764-foot Mt. Clements; and 9,604-foot Going-To-The-Sun-Mountain. A large variety of wildlife abounds in Glacier, and usually shy species such as bighorn sheep and mountain goat are easily photographed. Perhaps most famous — and most misunderstood — of the Park's animal community is the awesome and endangered grizzly bear. The great bear requires vast areas of wilderness for survival, and the existence of the bear here and elsewhere in the mountains of Montana gives testimony to the fact that such areas still remain. It is also a reminder of the responsibility Americans have to preserve these places in their natural condition forever.

Hikers on the trail to Sperry Chalet. (RON GLOVAN)

Top: Near the summit, on the first ascent of the north face of Mt. Cleveland. Rising 6,700 feet in four miles, it is the steepest uplift in the Northern Rockies. (STEVE JACKSON)
Bottom: Winter on the North Ridge of Mt. St. Nicholas. (RICK REESE) *Right: A shadow hangs over the imposing north face of Mt. Siyeh, first climbed in 1979.* (TERRY KENNEDY)

CHAPTER TEN

NORTHWEST OF YELLOWSTONE

The Madison, Gallatin, and Gravelly Ranges

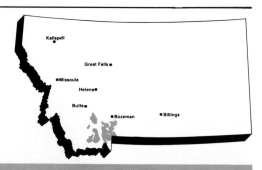

by Rick Reese

Above: Sunrise over Hilgard Peak (left) and the high peaks of the Madison Range. In 1983 Congress established the Lee Metcalf Wilderness here. (GEORGE WUERTHNER) *Opposite page: The Madison Range contains the Spanish Peaks Wilderness Area. This is Spanish Lakes in the afternoon light.* (PAT O'HARA)

Immediately northwest of Yellowstone Park lie two fault block massifs running generally north and south but separated into two distinct ranges by a long, prominent canyon. The Madison Range is the westernmost of the two and lies along the high divide between the Gallatin Canyon on the east and the Madison Valley on the west. The Gallatin Range comprises those peaks bordered by the Gallatin Canyon on the west and the Yellowstone River Valley on the east. Both the Madison and the Gallatin Rivers have their headwaters in these mountains and flow wildly northward to Three Forks where they join with the Jefferson River to form the beginning of the mighty Missouri River.

The Madison-Gallatin country comprises a major portion of the northwest corner of the Greater Yellowstone Ecosystem, the largest essentially intact ecosystem remaining in the temperate zones of the earth. Greater Yellowstone is a gigantic area encompassing up to ten million acres and stretching all the way from Bozeman, Montana on the north to beyond Jackson, Wyoming on the south. Within its confines are Grand Teton and Yellowstone National Parks, two national wildlife refuges and large portions of six national forests. These lands are highly interrelated biologically, and their environmental integrity, including the fragile resources of Yellowstone National Park itself, depend heavily upon wise resource management of each component. In this regard, the lands of the Madison-Gallatin country are inordinately important.

The Madison Range proper stretches for nearly 50 miles from its northernmost beginnings about 20

miles southwest of Bozeman to its terminus at Highway 287 and Hebgen Lake on the south. With six peaks above 11,000 feet, the Madison Range ranks as Montana's second highest. Within the Madison Range lie five major clusters of high peaks: the Spanish Peaks; the peaks just south of Jack Creek, including Lone Mountain, Fan Mountain, Cedar Mountain and Sphinx Mountain; the Taylor Peaks; the Hilgard Peaks; and the Monument Peaks. These clusters are separated by a series of canyons which begin high on the Madison crest and run east or west into the Gallatin and Madison Rivers respectively. Few of these drainages are roaded to any significant extent, and only at Big Sky does the road reach the hydrologic divide — elsewhere the Madison crest remains untouched. In 1983 Congress included 261,000 acres of the Madison Range in the Lee Metcalf Wilderness and designated an additional 38,000 acres in the southern end of the range as the "Cabin Creek Special Management Unit."

The Spanish Peaks dominate the northern end of the Madison Range. The imprint of recent alpine glaciation is clearly descernible here where some 25 peaks soar to more than 10,000 feet, including 11,015-foot Gallatin Peak, the highest in this area. Most of the Spanish Peaks are composed of ancient igneous and sedimentary rocks converted through the ages to gneiss and schist, and are some of the oldest exposed rocks on earth.

A portion of the Spanish Peaks and the Beartrap Canyon to the northwest are now included in the Lee Metcalf Wilderness. In the twenty miles from the bottom of the Beartrap Canyon to the crest of the Spanish Peaks, the terrain sweeps upward for 6,500 feet, one of the greatest elevation gradients in Montana.

72

The Spanish Peaks are separated from the rest of the Madison Range to the south by Jack Creek and the West Fork of the Gallatin River. Controversy has swirled around this area since the late '60s when plans for the construction of the enormous Big Sky resort were announced. Big Sky became a reality in the '70s, and in the early '80s the wild Madison was effectively cut in half when the Burlington Northern Company pushed their logging operations into the head of Jack Creek.

Between Jack Creek and Indian Creek lie four major peaks comprising the high central portion of the Madison Range: Fan Mountain, Lone Mountain, Cedar Mountain and Sphinx Mountain. All are prominent peaks when viewed from the Madison Valley on the west, but with the exception of Lone Mountain, they are hidden from the canyons of the east. The Taylor Peaks, a small group of high mountains surrounding 11,256-foot Koch Peak, lie immediately south of Indian Creek. The Hilgard Peaks lie south of the Taylor Peaks and north of Hebgen and Quake Lakes. At 11,316 feet, Hilgard Peak is the highest point in the Madison Range, and

Senator Lee Metcalf, 1911-1978.
(COURTESY OF DONNA METCALF)

Blue Danube Lake in the Lee Metcalf Wilderness. (GEORGE WUERTHNER)

"The death of Lee Metcalf stills a voice that had long spoken up for the great wilderness areas of this country. He came from the land of the Big Sky, of wide plains, of rugged mountains, where a traveler can go for miles without meeting another person." Thus spoke President Jimmy Carter the day Lee Metcalf died.

Lee Metcalf represented the people of Montana in Congress for a quarter of a century. During those years he emerged as a giant in the struggle to preserve a portion of America's wilderness heritage. Without him there would have been no Scapegoat Wilderness, no Wild and Scenic Missouri River, no Montana Wilderness Bill, and perhaps no Absaroka-Beartooth or Great Bear Wilderness areas.

"Thanks to Metcalf," wrote David Brower, "wilderness may have a chance to survive all the present generations, and to endure for all the answers it has to questions we have not yet learned how to ask, for all the coming generations, to keep the world from being a cage."

Lee Metcalf was also a man of uncompromising integrity who cared for honesty more than image, dignity more than publicity. A few days after his death, an editorial by Carl Rieckmann in the *Tobacco Valley News* in tiny Eureka, Montana said of Metcalf: "One thing is certain: You don't need to explain who he was and what he was about to a public which never had to scratch its head over where Lee Metcalf stood on issues ... love him or leave him, you didn't suffer from the aura of fuzzy uncertainty which sometimes surrounds politicians ... He acted like he felt. Lee Metcalf didn't pretend."

"His legacy," wrote Flynn Gill in the *Billings Gazette* on January 14, 1978, "may be thoughts young and old Americans think of him as they hike in Montana's mountains breathing clean air, or when they pause to sip from a clear stream tumbling down through a canyon."

The passing of Lee Metcalf left a void in American conservation that never can be filled. We may never look upon his like again.

second highest in Montana outside the Beartooth Range. The southwestern corner of the Madison holds thousands of acres of critical elk and grizzly habitat in an area known as the Monument Peaks.

East of the Gallatin Canyon the Gallatin Range rises to more than 10,000 feet, bordered on the east by the Yellowstone River Valley and stretching south from near Bozeman for nearly 60 miles all the way into the northwest corner of Yellowstone National Park. The topography of the Gallatin Range is somewhat less precipitous than the Madison Range, but it does include some spectacular peaks and high open ridges in the 20 miles from the Hyalite Peaks on the north to the mountains around Ramshorn Lake on the south. The rest of the range is a myriad of sheer canyons, lesser peaks and a huge expanse of largely roadless alpine and sub-alpine area.

Land ownership in the Gallatin, as in the Madison Range to the west, is a complicated mass of "checkerboard ownership," alternating sections of national forest and Burlington Northern Company lands. This pattern stems from government land grants made to the Northern Pacific Railway Company nearly a century ago as a means of stimulating the development of western railroads. The Burlington Northern Company (Northern Pacific's successor company) still owns tens of thousands of acres in the Gallatin and Madison Ranges within the boundaries of the national forest. Although cooperative management of these lands has prevailed in this century, recent conflicts have arisen as Burlington Northern has moved to log certain of its sections to what some feel is the detriment of surrounding public lands.

The Gallatin Range supports a large variety of wildlife, due partially to its proximity to Yellowstone Park and partially to its lack of development. Elk, deer, moose, mountain goat, bighorn sheep, and black and grizzly bear are found here as are a variety of raptors and game birds. Some evidence also suggests the presence of an extremely rare wolf and wolverine population as well as an occasional mountain lion.

A large portion of the Gallatin Range, the 151,000-acre Hyalite-Porcupine-Buffalo Horn area is under consideration for wilderness designation, and land use decisions reached in the '80s will have a definitive impact on the future of the area.

Above: The Gallatin Range near Gardiner. (TOM DIETRICH)
Left: Tom Miner Basin, a lonely open forested area high in the Gallatins. (GEORGE WUERTNER)

Above: In the Spanish Peaks. (TOM CORDINGLEY)
Right top: Storm clouds over peaks surrounding Hyalite Lake, Gallatin Range. (JOHN REDDY)
Right bottom: Above headwaters of Cottonwood Creek, Gallatin Range. (GEORGE WUERTHNER)

Above: Hyalite Lake. (JOHN REDDY)
Right: Black Butte in the Gravelly Range. (GEORGE WUERTHNER)

West across the Madison Valley and lying roughly parallel to the Madison River is the Gravelly Range. A lower, more gentle and heavily vegetated mountain chain than the Madison, the Gravellys parallel the Madison River from Virginia City to the Centennial Valley about 40 miles south. The dominant grasslands, broken by patches of aspen and conifer, provide superb grazing and wildlife habitat as well as some of Montana's finest big game hunting. An improved dirt road traverses much of the Gravelly crest and provides excellent sightseeing in the Gravellys as well as superb views of the Madison Range to the east. The nearby Snowcrest Range is considered by some to be a subsidiary range of the Gravellys.

South of the Madison Range across Quake Lake rise the Henry's Lake Mountains, which some persons regard as a southern extension of the Madison Range. Frequently referred to as the "Lionhead Area," after 9,574-foot Lionhead Mountain, 26,500 acres of this beautiful, isolated range just north of the Idaho border have been recommended for formal wilderness designation. Unstable geologic formations such as the one resulting in the catastrophic 1959 land slide at Quake Lake are common in these mountains. The United States Geological Survey has noted that an even larger slide could occur on Targhee Peak here in the Henry's Lake Mountains. Sheep Point (10,600 feet) and the spectacular Targhee Basin lie within the proposed Lionhead wilderness, an area which supports a significant population of bighorn sheep, occasional grizzly bears, and a variety of other wildlife.

Top: The "Lionhead Area" falls away to the north from the summit of Sheep Mountain. This pristine area in the Henry's Lake Mountains is a prime candidate for wilderness designation. (RICK REESE)
Bottom: Targhee Basin in the Lionhead area near the Montana-Idaho border west of Yellowstone National Park. (ED MADEJ)

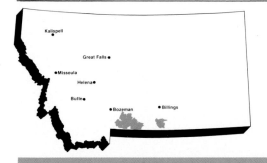

CHAPTER ELEVEN

THE ROOF OF MONTANA

Absaroka-Beartooth and the Isolated Pryors

by Rick Reese

Immediately north-northeast of Yellowstone National Park, and southwest of Billings, lies the enormous mountain uplift of the Absaroka and Beartooth Ranges, one of the highest, wildest and most awesome alpine areas of North America.

The Absaroka-Beartooth is bounded by the Yellowstone River and Paradise Valley on the west, by a diagonal line from Livingston on the northwest to beyond Red Lodge on the southeast, and by the Montana-Wyoming border on the south. It is an integral part of the Greater Yellowstone Ecosystem. For nearly 65 miles across its southern boundary not a single road penetrates more than a few short miles into the periphery of the mountains.

The Boulder River, which runs north into Montana out of the high country, is the approximate dividing line between the Absaroka Range on the west and the Beartooth Mountains on the east. The road along the river is one of the few signs of man throughout the 2,500 square miles of this country — the rest is in an essentially natural condition, little changed from the time of the earliest human visitation here thousands of years ago.

A large portion of the area, nearly one million acres, comprises the congressionally-created Absaroka-Beartooth Wilderness. Here at least, this land will remain pristine, untouched by the exploitation that has affected other mountain areas of the West.

The Beartooth Range and the incomparable Beartooth Plateau make up the eastern portion of the Absaroka-Beartooth. This is an area characterized by

A clearing storm lifts off a glacial lake in the Beartooth Mountains. (RICK REESE)

high peaks (29 of which exceed 12,000 feet, including Montana's highest mountain, 12,799-foot Granite Peak), expansive treeless tundra plateaus, deep canyons and hundreds of mountain lakes. Three-fourths of the country lies far above timberline where tumultuous wind and weather scour the land; annual snow accumulations of more than 200 inches are common. Geological diversity pervades the Beartooth Range where rocks have been dated to almost four billion years, some of the oldest

formations known to man. One can observe formations varying from precambrian to those of volcanic origin, and glaciers are still carving the cirques and canyons of the range.

The Beartooth Plateau once was covered by sediments thousands of feet thick. As the Beartooth uplifted and tilted south, these sediments slid into Wyoming, leaving a nearly flat plateau of hard, resistant, precambrian, igneous and metamorphic rock. Enormous glaciers covered nearly the entire

Beartooth Plateau and spilled down its sides, sometimes for miles into the surrounding plains. Large, flat-bottomed canyons visible today were carved from the mountainsides by these ancient glaciers.

The large peaks which today rise above the plateau are the last remnants of the sedimentary cover which once prevailed here. In time, they too will be reduced to nothing.

Opposite page: At nearly 12,000 feet in the Beartooth Mountains, Mt. Wilse is the table-top mountain in the upper right. (RICK GRAETZ)
This page, top: On the eastern margin of the Beartooth plateau. (RICK GRAETZ)
Bottom: A group of Montana Boy Scouts catch the last rays of evening sun on the Beartooth plateau. (RICK REESE)
Right: Above Wounded Man and Pinchot Lakes in the Beartooths. (RICK GRAETZ)

"Each ridge and possible approach to the top of the peak was as carefully scanned with glasses as time would permit, after which the party returned to camp just at dark, convinced that there was no easy way up Granite Peak and that the only way it would ever be climbed was through laborious effort intermingled with a lot of good luck and favorable weather conditions." Thus wrote a member of the first party to ascend Montana's highest mountain the night before the successful ascent on August 23, 1923. During the 30 years following the first ascent, Granite Peak was climbed by only 17 parties including those led by such famous American mountaineers as Norman Clyde, Robert Underhill, and Paul Petzoltd. Though not difficult by current mountaineering standards, the climb can be extremely dangerous for the inexperienced. Occasionally even more experienced climbers, such as the one pictured at left below, are killed or injured. This man suffered a fractured pelvis in a fall near the summit of the peak in August 1980 and lay on a ledge for two and a half days before being evacuated by rescuers in a dangerous helicopter operation.

(RICK REESE)

(RICK REESE)

Looking south across the town of Livingston to the uplift of the Absaroka Mountains. (TOM MURPHY)

The Absaroka Range comprises the western portion of the Absaroka-Beartooth. In contrast to the Beartooth Range, the Absaroka is predominantly forested, the terrain more gentle, the soil deeper, the vegetation more prevalent. Only one-fourth of the area here is above timberline, mostly on the high ridges and peaks. In several areas where the peaks do rise to high elevations they form impressive spires and crags. Large portions of the Absaroka are more remote, and more rarely visited, than even the Beartooth. The area is bordered by extremely rugged peaks and high passes on the west and north and by large roadless portions of Yellowstone Park on the south. During the National Roadless and Undeveloped Area Inventory (RARE) conducted by the U.S. Forest Service in the early '70s, the Absaroka Range was given the highest wilderness quality index rating in the entire country: 200 a scale of 200. In terms of the criteria used in the Forest Service inventory — scenic quality, variety and isolation — the Absaroka was, and remains today, unsurpassed.

The Absaroka-Beartooth is the headwaters for dozens of rivers and streams and encompasses some 340 lakes; as a high quality watershed it is an extremely important resource. Described by one geologist as the "most efficient hydrologic system we'll see in a few million years," the area acts as a huge natural generator, storage system and distribution network for water. Nine major drainages pour a million and a half acre feet of pure water out of their canyons annually, and more than one-third of the total flow of the Yellowstone River between Yellowstone Lake and Billings arises in the Absaroka-Beartooth.

Due east of the Beartooth Mountains about 30 miles across the fertile valley of the Clark's Fork of the

Above: The Boulder River and its falls at Natural Bridge (CHARLES KAY)
Right: Shell Mountain in the Absaroka Range. (SANDRA CAHILL)

Above: Sawtooth Mountain in the Absaroka Range near Livingston. (NEIL DUKE)
Left top: This magnificent pinnacle near Mt. Cowan in the Absaroka Range was first climbed in 1974. (RICK REESE)
The climbers pictured at left made the third ascent in 1984. (RICK REESE)

Yellowstone River, the Pryor Mountains are visible. Inconspicuous in comparison to the massive Beartooth and altogether different in character, the Pryors mark the last vestige of mountain country before the prairies and badlands of central and eastern Montana which dominate the landscape in a broad sweep all the way to the borders of the Dakotas.

The highest point in the Pryors is nearly 9,000 feet above sea level, but most of the range is considerably lower. It is a land of topographic diversity, featuring flat benches, mesas and buttes, high deserts, steeply dipping rimrocks and deep canyons. Along the southern slopes of the Pryors dry limestone canyons with their desert environments comprise an ecosystem not found elsewhere in Montana. Thirty-six thousand acres of the area have been proposed for wilderness designation.

The Pryor Mountains and nearby foothills are divided into four jurisdictional areas: a large portion of the northern mountains are on the Crow Indian Reservation, the high central mountains are on the Custer National Forest, the lower southernmost portions are managed by the Bureau of Land Management, and the National Park Service administers a small part of the eastern slopes adjacent to the Big Horn Canyon National Recreation Area.

In this area, long known for its unique archaeological sites and pre-historic habitation, very recent evidence suggests that ancient cave dwellers may have hunted mountain sheep here some 30,000 years ago. If so, they were by far the earliest known inhabitants of this entire region, pushing back earlier estimated dates of habitation by nearly 20,000 years.

Left: A wild horse roams the 32,000-acre Pryor Mountains Wild Horse Range of south-central Montana. The area was set aside in 1968 for the protection of wild horses, watershed, wildlife, archaeological sites and scenic values. (MICHAEL S. CRUMMETT)
Above: Autumn aspen stands in a blaze of color on the slopes of the Pryor Mountains near Pryor Gap. (MICHAEL S. CRUMMETT)
Right: The Pryor Mountains consist of large, broadly arched uplifts of the earth's crust and rise alone and isolated from the prairie of south-central Montana, where they abut the western edge of the Big Horn Canyon National Recreation Area (far right) (CHARLES KAY PHOTOS)

MONTANA'S MOUNTAINS

A Geographical Guide to Every Range in the Treasure State

compiled by Ed Madej

ABSAROKA RANGE A major mountain range, 150 miles long (50 miles in Montana), forming the eastern boundary of Yellowstone National Park. The Absaroka extends south from Livingston, Montana, to just north of Dubois, Wyoming. The highest summit is Francs Peak (13,153') in Wyoming; the highest summit in Montana is Mt. Cowen (11,206'). Absaroka is a Crow Indian name meaning "sharp-tailed bird."

ADEL MOUNTAINS Small range located near Craig and Wolf Creek along the Missouri River, known for its interesting volcanic formations, called laccoliths, which form flat-topped buttes.

ANACONDA RANGE Medium size mountain range along the Continental Divide southwest of the town of Anaconda, for which it is named. Two-thirds of the range is within the Anaconda-Pintler Wilderness; the highest summit is West Goat Peak (10,793').

APGAR MOUNTAINS Small range located just east of the North Fork of the Flathead River in Glacier National Park. Noted for its huckleberry crops and numerous grizzly bears.

BANGTAIL MOUNTAINS Popular name for the short range of mountains just east of the Bridger Range and north of Bozeman Pass.

BEARPAW MOUNTAINS Small, 25-mile-long range located southeast of Havre. Completely surrounded by prairie and cut off from the major range of the Rockies, most of the Bearpaws are the remains of ancient volcanoes.

BEARTOOTH RANGE Highest range in the state with 29 summits exceeding 12,000 feet including Granite Peak, the loftiest mountain in Montana at

Granite Peak, Beartooth Range. (GEORGE WUERTHNER)

12,799 feet. The Beartooths lie southwest of Billings and stretch for 50 miles east to west. The range features massive 10,000-foot high plateaus and hundreds of alpine lakes.

BEAVERHEAD RANGE A subrange of the Bitterroot Range, the Beaverheads run for 165 miles along the Continental Divide from Lost Trail Pass to Monida Pass forming the border between Montana and Idaho. Highest Peak is Scott Peak (11,393') which is one mile across the border in Idaho. The name Beaverhead was assigned to Beaverhead Rock by Lewis and Clark as they traveled up the Beaverhead River near present-day Dillon in 1805.

BELTON HILLS A group of low hills near West Glacier in Glacier National Park.

BIG BELT MOUNTAINS Major range running for 80 miles along the eastern shore of Canyon Ferry Reservoir and the Missouri River near Helena. Known for its interesting limestone canyons including the Gates of the Mountains, its highest point is Mt. Baldy (9,472').

BIGHORN MOUNTAINS Major range, almost entirely within Wyoming. Only the northern 20 miles of these mountains reach into Montana south of Billings.

BIG HOLE DIVIDE Range of mountains separating the headwaters of the Big Hole River from the tributaries of the Beaverhead River west of Dillon.

BIG SHEEP MOUNTAINS A series of badlands and low hills forming the drainage divide between the Missouri and Yellowstone Rivers north of Miles City.

BIG SNOWY MOUNTAINS Isolated 20-mile-long range of 8,000-foot peaks south of Lewistown. Known for the Knife Blade Ridge at their crest and for unusual ice caves.

BITTERROOT RANGE The longest mountain range in the state (450 miles long) stretching from Lookout Pass on the north to Raynolds Pass on the south and forming the border between Montana and Idaho. The Bitterroot Range is the most rugged border between any two states in the union, and the only state boundary which runs along the Continental Divide. The spectacular granitic peaks west of Hamilton in the Selway-Bitterroot Wilderness are usually referred to as the "main" Bitterroot; named after the bitterroot, Montana's official state flower.

BITTERROOT DIVIDE 1) The 7,000-foot ridge separating lower Rock Creek from the lower Bitterroot River drainage southeast of Missoula. 2) The long dividing ridge between the drainage of the Clearwater River and the Clark Fork in the Bitterroot Mountains northwest of Missoula.

BLACKTAIL MOUNTAINS A small range of 8,000-foot peaks extending for 20 miles in the area southeast of Dillon.

BOUNDARY MOUNTAINS A small clump of mountains, including Long Knife Peak, on the Canadian border in Glacier National Park north of Kintla Lake.

BRIDGER RANGE A group of nine-thousand-foot peaks, extending 25 miles north of Bozeman. Named for the frontiersman Jim Bridger, the Bridgers are known for steep mountainsides and their incredible powder snow, sometimes called "cold smoke."

BROAD VALLEY ROCKIES A physiographic term referring to the mountains in southwest Montana which form a "basin and range" type topography. All the ranges drained by the headwaters of the Missouri River (especially the Jefferson and part of the Madison Rivers) are encompassed in this area.

BUCKHORN MOUNTAINS A little-used name for a section of the Purcell Mountains including Northwest Peak, in the extreme northwestern corner of Montana.

BULL MOUNTAINS A 40-mile-long range of 4,000-foot hills north of Billings, forming the drainage divide between the Yellowstone and Musselshell Rivers.

CABINET MOUNTAINS A major range of extremely steep peaks in northwestern Montana west of Libby. Snowshoe Peak (8,738') is the highest in the range and the highest summit between the Continental

Heavenly Twin Peaks, Bitterroot Range. (JOHN KREMPEL)

Divide on the east and the Cascade Range on the west. The range is essentially divided into two parts, the West Cabinets or "Scotchman Peaks" and the higher East Cabinets within the Cabinet Mountain Wilderness. Named by early French trappers who thought their rock formations resembled wooden cabinets.

CASTLE MOUNTAINS A small group of rolling hills and jagged limestone spires (which resemble castles) located southeast of White Sulphur Springs.

Mount Cowan in the Absaroka Range. (RICK GRAETZ)

CAYUSE HILLS Low range of hills on the drainage divide between the Musselshell River and the Yellowstone River north of Big Timber and east of the Crazy Mountains.

CENTENNIAL MOUNTAINS A subrange of the Bitterroots, running east to west for 50 miles on the Montana-Idaho border between Monida Pass and Red Rock Pass. Known for their extremely abrupt northern escarpment, the mountains were named for the Centennial Valley, which they border on the south.

CHALK BUTTES or **CHALK CLIFFS** A small group of 4,000-foot buttes south of Ekalaka in the southeastern corner of Montana.

CHINESE WALL A thousand-foot-high limestone cliff running along the Continental Divide for nearly 25 miles in the heart of the Bob Marshall Wilderness.

COEUR D'ALENE MOUNTAINS A major range of 5,000 to 7,000'-peaks extending for 75 miles between the lower Clark Fork River and the St. Regis River south of Thompson Falls. The mountains run from the southeast near the town of St. Regis to the northwest where they pass into northern Idaho.

COLUMBIA ROCKIES A physiographic term referring to the mountains of northwest Montana which are drained by tributaries of the Columbia River (e.g. the Clark Fork, Kootenai, and Flathead Rivers). Includes such ranges as the Cabinets, the Coeur D'Alenes, the northern Bitterroots, the Missions, and the western sides of Glacier National Park as well as the Bob Marshall Wilderness.

COMO PEAKS A small group of spectacular granitic peaks west of Darby in the Selway-Bitterroot Wilderness; elevations exceed 9,000 feet.

CONTINENTAL DIVIDE The hydrologic dividing line in the western United States which forms the crest of the Rocky Mountains and separates rivers which flow west into the Pacific Ocean from rivers which flow east into the Atlantic by way of the Gulf of Mexico. Nearly 800 miles of the divide is within Montana or on its border, more than in any other western state.

CONTINENTAL DIVIDE RANGE An unofficial term for the mountains forming the Continental Divide between Marias Pass and Rogers Pass in the Bob Marshall, Great Bear, and Scapegoat Wilderness Areas.

CRAZY MOUNTAINS A group of spectacular alpine peaks located northeast of Livingston. The highest summit is Crazy Peak (11,214'). The Crazy Mountains are glacial-carved remnants of igneous intrusions.

DEER CREEK MOUNTAINS A popular name for the hills north of the Beartooth Range and south of the Yellowstone River south of Big Timber. Highest summit is Sugarloaf Mtn. (7,950').

DEER LODGE MOUNTAINS A little-used term for the range of hills forming the eastern side of the Deer Lodge Valley and running north to south from Avon to Butte.

DRY LAKE MOUNTAINS A tiny range of hills in the northern foothills of the Tobacco Root Mountains south of Whitehall.

DRY RANGE A very small range of inconspicuous hills northwest of White Sulphur Springs and sandwiched between the Adel Mountains on the north, the Big Belt Mountains on the west, and the Smith River and Little Belt Mountains on the east.

EISENHOWER MOUNTAINS This unofficial geographic name was applied to the unnamed mountains between Helena and Deer Lodge during the 1950s and '60s. It was part of an unsuccessful attempt to begin naming some Montana mountain ranges after U.S. Presidents and historical figures.

ELKHORN MOUNTAINS A group of mountains south and slightly east of Helena known for abundant wildlife. Highest summit is Crow Peak (9,414'), named by Lewis and Clark in 1805.

FLATHEAD ALPS A small group of extremely remote 8,000-foot peaks located between the South Fork of the Flathead River and the Continental Divide in the heart of the Bob Marshall Wilderness.

FLATHEAD RANGE A major range of mountains running for 60 miles southeast of West Glacier into the Great Bear and Bob Marshall Wilderness areas. The Flathead Range divides the South Fork from the Middle Fork of the Flathead River and is named after the Flathead Indians. Highest summit is Silvertip Mtn. (8,890').

FLINT CREEK RANGE An alpine range 25 miles long which forms the western side of the Deer Lodge Valley; highest summit is Mt. Powell (10,164').

GALLATIN RANGE A major range of 10,000-foot peaks running from south of Bozeman for 60 miles into Yellowstone National Park. Highest summit is Electric Peak (10,992'). Named by Lewis and Clark for Albert Gallatin, Secretary of War under Thomas Jefferson.

GALTON RANGE A subrange of the Whitefish Range located to the west of the main crest of the Whitefish and east of Eureka; includes the well-known Ten Lakes Scenic Area.

GARDEN WALL An extremely steep five-mile escarpment located north of Logan Pass in Glacier National Park. A rock face north of Mountaineer Peak in the Mission Mountains also bears this name.

GARFIELD PEAKS An unofficial name for the collection of 10,000-foot peaks west of Monida Pass on the Idaho border; includes the Lima Peaks and the Red Conglomerate Peaks. Highest summit is Garfield Mtn. (10,935').

GARNET RANGE An east- to west-trending range of mountains which runs for 60 miles between the Blackfoot River and the Clark Fork River. These 7,000-foot mountains are known for such ghost towns as Garnet and Coloma.

GRANITE RANGE This subrange of the Beartooth Mountains is found between West Rosebud Creek and the Stillwater River. It is one of only three clusters of peaks in the state with summits over twelve thousand feet; Mt. Wood (12,661') is the highest summit.

GRAVE CREEK RANGE A 15-mile-long subrange of the Bitterroot Mountains located just west of Missoula; highest summit is Petty Mtn. (7,265').

Frazier Lake in the Bridger Mountains. (PHIL FARNES)

GRAVELLY RANGE A high rolling plateau-like range of 10,000-foot peaks south of Virginia City and west of the Madison River; known for its extensive parks, meadows and big game.

GREENHORN RANGE A subrange of the Gravelly Range located to the northwest of the main Gravellys and southwest of Virginia City.

HANGING GARDEN WALL The 11,000-foot cliff that runs between Mt. Hague and Mt. Wood in the Granite Range of the Beartooth Mountains.

HENRY'S LAKE MOUNTAINS The semi-circle of 10,000-foot peaks along the Continental Divide near Henry's Lake, Idaho. This is a poorly defined range which includes part of the eastern Centennial Mountains and perhaps part of the southern Madison

Range. The northernmost of these peaks are unofficially called the Lionhead Mountains; highest summit is Sheep Point (10,600').

HIGHLAND MOUNTAINS A small range of 10,000-foot peaks located south of Butte; highest summit is Table Mtn. (10,223').

HIGHWOOD MOUNTAINS An isolated group of 7,000-foot mountains which emerge out of the plains east of Great Falls; considered to be the remnants of ancient volcanoes.

HILGARD PEAKS The highest group of 11,000-foot peaks in the Madison Range directly north of Earthquake Lake. Hilgard Peak (11,316') is the highest peak in Montana outside the Beartooth Range.

In the Snowcrest Range. (JIM WRIGHT)

HORSESHOE HILLS A low range of hills separating the Missouri River from the Gallatin Valley northwest of Bozeman.

HORN MOUNTAINS A tiny range of mountains connecting the Henry's Lake Mountains to the Gravelly Range just west of Raynolds Pass.

HUDSON BAY DIVIDE The hydrologic divide running north from Triple Divide Peak in Glacier National Park and separating the rivers which run into Hudson Bay from those draining to the Gulf of Mexico. Montana is the only state with rivers running to the Pacific, the Atlantic and Hudson Bay.

HYALITE PEAKS A group of extremely scenic 10,000-foot peaks at the northern end of the Gallatin Range and immediately south of Bozeman.

IRONROD HILLS Small range of hills on the eastern slope of the Highland Mountains due west of Silver Star.

ITALIAN PEAKS An unofficial name for a subrange of the Beaverhead and Bitterroot Ranges in the extreme southwest corner of the state. These little-known peaks contain the only 11,000-foot peaks in the entire Bitterroot Range including the highest, Scott Peak (11,393'), whose summit lies one mile inside Idaho.

JOHN LONG MOUNTAINS A short range of mountains paralleling the Sapphire Range to the east and located between Rock Creek and the Phillipsburg Valley. The 30-mile-long range has few summits above 7,000 feet.

JUDITH MOUNTAINS A small range located northeast of Lewistown and several miles due east of the Judith River.

KELLY HILLS Eroded ridgetops northwest of Big Timber and the southern slope of the Crazy Mountains.

LARB HILLS A series of eroded hills on the southern reaches of the Milk River Valley west of Glasgow.

LEWIS RANGE The 65-mile-long main range of Glacier National Park. These mountains are named after Captain Meriwether Lewis; highest summit is Mt. Cleveland (10,466').

LIMA PEAKS A series of 10,000-foot peaks northwest of Monida Pass. Sometimes referred to as the Garfield Peaks.

LIMESTONE HILLS A range of low hills between the Elkhorn Mountains and the Missouri River west of Townsend.

LIMESTONE PALISADES A series of limestone cliffs extending for several miles in the foothills of the Beartooth Range west of Red Lodge.

LIONHEAD MOUNTAINS Unofficial name for the highest portion of the Henry's Lake Mountains just west of West Yellowstone and south of Earthquake Lake. Sometimes considered to be a southern extension of the Madison Range, the Lionhead boasts half a dozen peaks above ten thousand feet, most of them along the Continental Divide.

LITTLE BELT A major range of mountains south of Great Falls which runs for 70 miles from the Smith River on the west to Judith Gap on the east; highest summit is Yogo Peak (8,801').

LITTLE BITTERROOT MOUNTAINS A small range located on the Flathead Indian Reservation west of the Little Bitterroot River between the southern Cabinet Mountains and the southern Salish Mountains.

LITTLE ROCKIES An isolated prairie range located southwest of Malta; known for its gold mines.

LITTLE SHEEP MOUNTAINS A low range of eroded badlands just south of the Big Sheep Mountains on the drainage divide between the Yellowstone and Missouri Rivers north of Miles City.

LITTLE SNOWY MOUNTAINS An eastern and lower offshoot of the Big Snowy Mountains which runs for 12 miles east to west in the area southeast of Lewistown.

LIVINGSTON RANGE The smaller of the two major ranges in Glacier National Park, the Livingston Range is located to the west of the Lewis Range and is about 35 miles long. Heavens Peak (8,987') is probably its most well-known and most photographed mountain.

LONDON HILLS A group of dry limestone hills south of the Jefferson River near Lewis and Clark Caverns just east of Cardwell.

MADISON RANGE This is essentially the second highest mountain range in Montana. The Madison range forms the high divide which runs for nearly 60 miles between the Gallatin Canyon on the east and the Madison Valley on the west. The highest summit and the highest peak in Montana outside the Beartooth Range is Hilgard Peak (11,316'). The range is composed of four or five subranges: the Spanish Peaks, the Taylor Peaks, the Hilgard Peaks, the Monument Peaks and perhaps the Lionhead Mountains, depending upon how one defines the

Granite outcropping in the Madison Range. (JOHN REDDY)

Madison's southern boundary. Most of the range is within the Lee Metcalf Wilderness. The range was named by Lewis and Clark for President James Madison.

McGILLIVRAY MOUNTAINS This is a little-used name for a portion of the Purcell Mountains north of the Kootenai River and west of Eureka.

MIDDLE ROCKIES A physiographic term (used interchangeably with the "Central Rockies") referring to those ranges between the northern and southern Rockies. The Middle Rockies extend from the Uinta and Wasatch ranges in Utah on the south, to the Absaroka and Beartooth Ranges on the north.

MISSION MOUNTAINS A spectacular 60-mile-long alpine range which divides the Swan Valley from the lower Flathead Valley and Flathead Lake. Long known for its beautiful high country and glaciated peaks, the Missions were named after the Jesuit mission at St. Ignatius which was founded in 1854; highest summit is McDonald Peak (9,820').

MISSOURI BREAKS The series of heavily eroded badlands along the Missouri River between Fort Benton and Fort Peck.

MOCCASIN MOUNTAINS A small range of hills northwest of Lewistown and divided into the north and south Moccasin Mountains by Warm Springs Creek.

The Mission Mountains. (RICK GRAETZ)

MONUMENT PEAKS A sub-unit of the Lee Metcalf Wilderness located immediately north of West Yellowstone. Monument Peaks may be viewed as an extension of either the Madison Range or the Gallatin Range; highest summit is Sage Peak (10,664').

NINEMILE DIVIDE The range of peaks dividing a portion of the Clark Fork River drainage from the Ninemile Creek drainage west of Missoula.

NORTHERN ROCKIES A physiographic term for the mountains north and northwest of Yellowstone National Park and extending through Montana, Idaho, northeastern Washington, British Columbia and Alberta.

OIL HILLS Small group of 6,000-foot hills southwest of Ringling and west of the Crazy Mountains.

PINTLER RANGE A name generally referring to the western extremities of the Anaconda Range above the Big Hole Valley; named after Charles Pintler, a Big Hole rancher.

PINE HILLS A popular name for the pine-covered plateaus and eroded badlands southeast of Miles City.

PINEY BUTTES The series of buttes and badlands located south of Fort Peck Reservoir and north of Jordan.

PIONEER MOUNTAINS A range of mountains northwest of Dillon which is bounded on three sides by the large U-shaped bend of the Big Hole River. The Range is split by the Wise River into eastern and western sub-ranges. The West Pioneers are a high rolling plateau, while the East Pioneers are a jagged alpine range with the highest summit being Tweedy Mtn. (11,154').

PRYOR MOUNTAINS A small group of limestone peaks and mesas located south of Billings near the Wyoming border. The highest summits reach nearly nine thousand feet. The Pryors are known for their mysterious ice caves and wild horses.

PURCELL MOUNTAINS A major range of mountains beginning at the northern banks of the Kootenai River and running north into British Columbia. Although fairly low and timbered in Montana and rarely reaching above seven thousand feet, the Purcells become higher and much more rugged in Canada.

RATTLESNAKE MOUNTAINS The range of hills forming the northern skyline of Missoula. They are named after Rattlesnake Creek which twists like a

The Smith River in the Little Belt Mountains. (MIKE MELOY)

snake through the mountains; highest summit is McLeod Peak.

RED CONGLOMERATE PEAKS A series of 10,000-foot peaks on the Continental Divide west of Monida Pass; sometimes called the Garfield Peaks.

REES HILLS Six-thousand-foot hills southeast of Ringling near the Crazy Mountains.

RESERVATION DIVIDE The mountains which separate Ninemile Creek from the lower Flathead River northwest of Missoula and form the southern boundary of the Flathead Indian Reservation. Squaw Peak (7,996') is the most prominent summit.

RINGING ROCKS A group of granitic spires northeast of Homestake Pass near Butte.

ROBERT E. LEE RANGE This unofficial name was applied to the mountains in the vicinity of Stemple Pass south of Lincoln during the 1950s or '60s in an unsuccessful attempt to name some Montana mountain ranges after famous historical figures and U.S. Presidents.

ROCKY MOUNTAINS The major mountain system along the Continental Divide in the western U.S. and Canada. The Rockies cover an area from northern New Mexico on the south to northern British Columbia on the north. Geologists divide the Rockies into three major parts based upon their geologic history. The Southern Rockies include the mountains of New Mexico and Colorado; the Middle or Central Rockies include the ranges of northern Utah, northwest Wyoming, eastern Idaho and the Absarokas and Beartooths in Montana; the Northern Rockies include the remainder of Montana and Idaho, northeastern Washington and the Canadian Rockies. The entire mountain system extending from Mexico to Alaska is more accurately referred to as the Western Cordillera of North America.

The Mission Mountains. (WILLIAM R. MUNOZ.)

ROCKY MOUNTAIN FRONT A name used to refer to the front range of mountains abutting the eastern side of the Bob Marshall Wilderness and stretching for 100 miles from Rogers Pass to Marias Pass; also called the Sawtooth Range, the highest summit is Rocky Mountain Peak (9,392').

ROSEBUD MOUNTAINS A low range of 5,000-foot mountains southeast of Harding near the Custer Battlefield.

RUBY MOUNTAINS A small range of mountains about 15 miles long and lying southwest of Virginia City. The highest peak here is well above 9,000'.

SALISH MOUNTAINS A range of heavily timbered hills running for 100 miles from south of Eureka to west of Polson and Flathead Lake. The highest summits are below 7,000 feet. Known for their many large lakes, these mountains were named for the Salish Indians.

SAPPHIRE MOUNTAINS A range of wooded hills 85 miles long which forms the eastern boundary of the Bitterroot Valley and the western side of Rock Creek Canyon. Noted for its abundant populations of elk and moose; the highest summit reaches just under 9,000 feet.

SAWTOOTH RANGE The official (though rarely used) name for the Rocky Mountain Front, this range is named after Sawtooth Mountain, a prominent peak at the mouth of the Sun River Canyon.

SCOTCHMAN PEAKS Popular name used to refer to the West Cabinet Mountains south of Troy. Known for the immense western red cedars found there, the highest summit in the area is Scotchman Peak (7,009') just over the border in Idaho.

SCRATCHGRAVEL HILLS A small range of hills in the west central portion of the Helena Valley. The remnants of an old volcano, the Scratchgravels reach a height of 5,253' and are named for the gold miners who scratched in the gravel of the Helena Valley in the 1860s and '70s.

SHINING MOUNTAINS The original name used by the early trappers for the Rocky Mountains.

SNOWCREST RANGE A 25-mile-long range of ten thousand foot peaks, south of Virginia City along the western edge of the Gravelly Range. Sometimes considered to be a subrange of the Gravellys, the jagged peaks of the Snowcrest reach their highest point at Sunset Peak (10,573').

SNOWY RANGE A name formerly used to refer to the north Absaroka and Beartooth Mountains.

SPANISH BREAKS The northern foothills of the Spanish Peaks in the Madison Range south of Bozeman.

SPANISH PEAKS The northernmost group of 10,000 and 11,000-foot peaks in the Madison Range. This very popular alpine hiking area is named for the Spanish trappers who visited the area around 1820; highest summit is Gallatin Peak (11,015').

SPOKANE HILLS The low range of hills that separates the Helena Valley on the west from the Townsend Valley on the southeast.

STONY MOUNTAINS The name used by the famous nineteenth-century explorer and geographer John Wesley Powell to describe the present-day Northern Rockies.

SWAN RANGE A major mountain range stretching for 100 miles and forming much of the western boundary of the Bob Marshall Wilderness. Known for its exquisite alpine and subalpine lakes such as those found in Jewel Basin, the highest summit in the Swan is Holland Peak (9,356').

SWEETGRASS HILLS An isolated range of prairie mountains on the Canadian border east of Glacier National Park. Elevations here reach nearly seven thousand feet.

TAYLOR PEAKS A group of 11,000-foot peaks in the Madison Range north of the Hilgard Peaks; highest summit is Koch Peak (11,286').

TENDOY MOUNTAINS A small range of mountains running 30 miles down the western side of Red Rock River near Lima; highest summit is (9,674').

THOMPSON PEAKS A group of peaks in the southern Salish Mountains west of Polson.

TOBACCO ROOT MOUNTAINS A dense cluster of ten-thousand-foot peaks southwest of Bozeman. This high range is noted for its numerous alpine lakes; highest summit is Mt. Jefferson (10,600').

TRILOBITE RANGE An extremely remote range on the boundary between the Bob Marshall and Great Bear Wildernesses. Named for the numerous trilobite fossils found there, the highest summit is Pentagon Mtn. (8,877').

WEST BIG HOLE MOUNTAINS A subrange of the Beaverhead and Bitterroot Mountains which runs for 55 miles from Lost Trail Pass on the north to Lemhi Pass on the south. Known for their splendid alpine scenery along the Continental Divide, the highest summit is Homer Youngs Peak (10,621').

WEST BOULDER DIVIDE The drainage divide between Little Mission Creek and the West Boulder River in the northern Absaroka Mountains near Livingston.

WHITE CLIFFS A series of chalk-like cliffs along the wild and scenic segment of the Missouri River east of Fort Benton.

WHITE HILLS A very small group of hills south of the Blacktail Mountains and southeast of Dillon.

WHITEFISH RANGE A major range of heavily timbered mountains which extends for 60 miles from Columbia Falls north to the Canadian Border. Portions of this range in the area west of Glacier National Park are notable for their dense populations of grizzly bears. The portion of the Whitefish Range in British Columbia is sometimes called the McDonald Range; highest summit in Montana is Nasukoin Mtn. (8,095').

WOLF MOUNTAINS A tiny range of prairie hills south of the Rosebud Mountains between Hardin, Montana and Sheridan, Wyoming.

YELLOWSTONE ROCKIES A term referring to the ranges of the Middle Rockies surrounding Yellowstone National Park and including the Madison, Gallatin, Beartooth, Absaroka, Teton, Gros Ventre, Wind River, Hoback, Wyoming, and Salt River Ranges.

NOTES ON MONTANA'S HIGHEST RANGES

compiled by Ed Madej

1. The Beartooth Range The Beartooths are the only range in the state with peaks over 12,000 feet in altitude. The Beartooths are such a high and massive range that even entire plateaus (some eleven of them) soar to heights greater than 10,000 feet. Eleven of the 29 peaks that exceed 12,000 feet are unnamed, including the state's sixth highest mountain. The Beartooths have been poorly surveyed by cartographers, and many elevations are probably innacurate.

2. The Madison Range Essentially the second highest range in the state, the Madisons have six peaks higher than 11,000 feet. Of the 122 peaks which exceed 10,000 feet, 74 are unnamed. (The Lionhead Mountains are included with the Madisons in these peak totals.) Hilgard Peak is the highest peak in the state outside of the Beartooths and the 61st highest peak in the state.

3. The Crazy Mountains The remnants of igneous intrusions make up the 10,000-foot peaks of the Crazies, 15 of which are unnamed. The Crazy Mountains feature some spectacular alpine peaks including 11,214-foot Crazy Peak.

4. The Absaroka Range The Absarokas have more 10,000-foot peaks (166+) than any other range in the state. They are the most poorly mapped and possibly the most rugged mountains in Montana. Most maps of this range were drawn in the 1930s and early '40s. One hundred twenty-eight major summits are without names here.

5. The East Pioneer Mountains Probably one of the lesser known of Montana's highest ranges, the East Pioneers have 50 summits over 10,000 feet.

Hilgard Peak and Hilgard Lake in the Madison Range.
(RICK GRAETZ)

6. The Bitterroot Range Montana's longest mountain range, the Bitterroot Range, also encompasses the Beaverhead and Centennial Mountains. The two highest summits (Scott and Weber Peaks) lie one mile inside Idaho, making Eighteenmile Peak the highest of the Bitterroots in Montana and the highest peak on the Continental Divide in the state. All of the Bitterroot's 11,000-foot peaks are in the little-known Italian Peaks Proposed Wilderness.

7. The Gallatin Range A major range of 10,000-foot peaks stretching for 60 miles south of Bozeman into Yellowstone National Park. The Gallatin Range's highest peak, Electric Peak (10,992'), lies just inside Yellowstone National Park.

8. The Anaconda Range A medium-sized range which straddles the Continental Divide southwest by Anaconda, Montana. A third of the 10,000-foot peaks here, including Mt. Haggin (second highest peak in the range), lie outside the federally designated Anaconda-Pintler Wilderness area.

9. The Tobacco Root Mountains A very compact, high range, the Tobacco Roots are unusual among Montana's highest ranges in that nearly every one of their 10,000-foot peaks is named. This is probably due to the long history of mining in these mountains, which are very close to the 19th-century boom town of Virginia City. The range is notable for its dense cluster of 10,000-foot peaks and numerous alpine lakes.

10. The Gravelly Range This high, rolling plateau-like range of 10,000-foot peaks is situated west of the Madison River and features extensive high parks and meadows. (The peak totals for this range include the 10,000-foot peaks from the subsidiary Snowcrest Range as well.)

11. The Glacier Park Mountains Glacier's mountains, while not the state's highest, are probably the steepest. On the western side of the park, Mt. Stimson and Mt. Jackson tower 6,800 to 7,000 feet over the valleys at their base. This elevation difference exceeds that of the eastern Beartooths, where Montana's highest peaks soar 6,000 to 6,500 feet over their accompanying valleys. The peaks of Glacier include the 10,000-foot peaks of the Lewis and Livingston Ranges.

12. The Highland Mountains This relatively small range south of Butte features the 10,000-foot-high plateau of aptly named Table Mountain.

13. The Flint Creek Range This small alpine range extends for 25 miles along the west side of the Deer Lodge Valley and is the only range in Montana with just one 10,000-foot peak, Mt. Powell (10,164').

NOTE: Early maps of the Mission Mountains, such as Hal Kanzler's 1963 recreation map, show the east summit of McDonald Peak to be 10,300 feet. More recent maps show this summit to be 9,820 feet and the Missions are therefore not included among the 10,000-foot ranges.

Windstorm just below the summit of Eighteenmile Peak in the Beaverhead Range, during a winter ascent. (RICK REESE)

MONTANA'S HIGHEST RANGES
The Mountains with Peaks above Ten Thousand Feet

Range	Highest Peak		10,000' to 10,999'	11,000' to 11,999'	12,000' and over	Total
1. Beartooth Range	Granite Peak	12,799'	45	46	29	120
2. Madison Range	Hilgard Peak	11,316'	122	6		128
3. Crazy Mountains	Crazy Peak	11,214'	24	1		25
4. Absaroka Range	Mt. Cowan	11,206'	164+	2+		166+
5. East Pioneer Mountains	Tweedy Mtn.	11,154'	48	2		50
6. Bitterroot Range	Eighteenmile Peak	11,141'	14	2*		16
	Scott Peak	11,393'				
7. Gallatin Range	Electric Peak	10,992'	15			15
8. Anaconda Range	West Goat Peak	10,793'	17			17
9. Tobacco Root Mountains	Mt. Jefferson	10,604'	26			26
10. Gravelly Range	Sunset Peak (Snowcrest Range)	10,581'	13			13
11. Glacier Park Mountains	Mt. Cleveland	10,466'	5			5
12. Highland Mountains	Table Mtn.	10,223'	4			4
13. Flint Creek Range	Mt. Powell	10,164'	1			1
	Totals		498+	59+	29	586+

Does not include two 11,000-foot peaks in the Bitterroot Range whose summits lie just across the Idaho border.

Note: Several major ranges do not make this "Highest Ranges" list. Such ranges as the Mission Mountains, the Cabinets, the Swan Range and other mountains of the Bob Marshall, while steep and beautiful, actually have fairly low (8,000' to 9,600') summits by Rocky Mountain standards.

MONTANA'S 100 HIGHEST MOUNTAINS

#	Name	Detail	Elevation	Range
1.	Granite Peak	(Southeast Peak)	12,799'	Beartooth
		(Northwest Peak)	12,710'	
2.	Mt. Wood	(Southeast Peak)	12,661'	Beartooth
		(Northwest Peak)	12,320'	
3.	Castle Mtn.		12,612'	Beartooth
4.	Whitetail Peak		12,548'	Beartooth
5.	Silver Run Peak	(West Peak)	12,542'	Beartooth
		(East Peak)	12,500'	
6.	Unnamed		12,529'	Beartooth
7.	Tempest Mtn.		12,478'	Beartooth
8.	Mt. Peal		12,415'	Beartooth
		(East Peak, "Mt. Pleasant")	12,006'	
9.	Castle Rock Mtn.	(South Peak)	12,408'	Beartooth
		(West Peak, "Darlene Mountain")	12,160'+	
		(North Peak)	12,000'+	
		(Northeast Peak)	12,000'	
10.	Beartooth Mtn.	(North Peak)	12,377'	Beartooth
		(South Peak, "Avalanche Mtn.")	12,010'	
11.	Glacier Peak		12,351'	Beartooth
12.	Bowback Mtn.	(North Peak)	12,343'	Beartooth
		(South Peak)	12,320'	
		(Middle Peak)	12,320'	
13.	Mt. Villard	(North Peak)	12,337'	Beartooth
		(West Peak, "Hidden Glacier Peak")	12,319'	
		(North Tower)	12,000'	
		(South Tower)	12,000'	
14.	Mt. Hague		12,328'	Beartooth
15.	Sundance Mtn.	(East Peak)	12,272'	Beartooth
		(West Peak)	12,206'	
16.	Salo Mtn.	(unofficial name)	12,240'+	Beartooth
17.	Ikerman Mtn.	(unofficial name, n. of Cairn Lake)	12,214'	Beartooth
18.	Mt. Rearguard		12,204'	Beartooth
19.	Elk Mtn.		12,192'	Beartooth
20.	Pyramid Mtn.	(West Peak, "Sacrifice")	12,151' / 12,027'	Beartooth
21.	Drop Off Mtn.	(unofficial name, s. of Beartooth Mountain)	12,117'	Beartooth
22.	Mystic Mtn.		12,063'	Beartooth
23.	Metcalf Mtn.	(unofficial name, s. of Frosty L.)	12,019'	Beartooth
24.	Hopper Mtn.	(unofficial name)	12,000'+	Beartooth
25.	Sylvan Peak		11,943'	Beartooth
26.	Mt. Inabnit		11,924'+	Beartooth
27.	Snowbank Mtn.		11,920'+	Beartooth
28.	Wolf Mtn.		11,840'	Beartooth
29.	Unnamed		11,836'	Beartooth
30.	Stillwater Plateau		11,820'	Beartooth
31.	Fishtail Plateau		11,808'	Beartooth
32.	Twin Peaks		11,800'	Beartooth
33.	Froze-to-Death Mtn.		11,765'	Beartooth
34.	Mt. Wilse		11,760'	Beartooth
35.	Medicine Mtn.		11,680'	Beartooth
36.	Summit Mtn.		11,680'	Beartooth
37.	Mt. Lockhart		11,647'	Beartooth
38.	Sawtooth, N. Peak	(unofficial name)	11,600'+	Beartooth
39.	Unnamed		11,638'	Beartooth
40.	Unnamed	(s. of Arch Lake)	11,563'	Beartooth
41.	Mt. Zimmer		11,550'	Beartooth
42.	Unnamed	(n. of Mystic Mtn.)	11,550'	Beartooth
43.	Iceberg Peak		11,520'	Beartooth
44.	Little Park Mtn.	(Middle Peak)	11,506'	Beartooth
45.	Sawtooth Mtn.		11,489'	Beartooth
46.	Mt. Hole-in-the-Wall		11,475'	Beartooth
47.	Thunder Mtn.		11,446'	Beartooth
48.	Unnamed	(North Peak of Little Park Mtn.)	11,441'	Beartooth
49.	Unnamed	(South Peak of Little Park Mtn.)	11,440'	Beartooth
50.	Mt. Dewey		11,436'	Beartooth
51.	Unnamed	("State Line Pk.")	11,415'	Beartooth
52.	Lonesome Mtn.		11,409'	Beartooth
53.	Unnamed	(S.E. Peak of Big Mountain)	11,389'	Beartooth
54.	Unnamed	(N. Peak of Hague)	11,384'	Beartooth
55.	Big Mtn.	(Main Peak)	11,371'	Beartooth
		(Far N.E. Peak)	11,156'	
56.	Unnamed		11,360'	Beartooth
57.	Tumble Mtn.		11,323'	Beartooth

58. Hilgard Peak	(Highest peak outside of the Beartooth Range)	11,316'	Madison
59. Mt. Douglas		11,298'	Beartooth
60. Koch Peak		11,286'	Madison
61. Unnamed	(close N.E. Peak of Big Mtn.)	11,280'+	Beartooth
62. Mt. Fox		11,245'	Beartooth
63. Unnamed	(E. Peak of Little Park Mountain)	11,225'	Beartooth
64. Crazy Peak		11,214'	Crazy
65. Echo Peak		11,214'	Madison
66. Imp Peak		11,212'	Madison
67. Mt. Cowan		11,206'	Absaroka
68. Two Sisters		11,188'	Beartooth
	(Sister Plateau)	11,138'	
69. Lone Mtn.		11,166'	Madison
70. Tweedy Mtn.		11,154'	East Pioneer
71. Chalice Peak		11,153'	Beartooth
72. Torrey Mtn.		11,147'	East Pioneer
73. Eighteenmile Peak	(Highest peak on Montana portion of the Continental Divide)	11,141'	Bitterroot
74. Mt. Rosebud		11,120'	Beartooth
75. Unnamed	(South Peak of Mt. Douglas)	11,112'	Beartooth
76. Unnamed	(Woodbine Falls Divide)	11,087'	Beartooth
77. Grass Mtn.		11,065'	Beartooth
78. Sawtooth Ridge		11,040'+	Madison
79. Cottonwood Peak		11,024'	Bitterroot
80. Gallatin Peak		11,015'	Madison
81. The Black Spire	(unofficial name)	11,002'	Absaroka
82. Italian Peak		10,998'	Bitterroot
83. Monument Peak		10,995'	Absaroka
84. Electric Peak		10,992'	Gallatin
85. Dutchman Peak		10,991'	Madison
86. Hodges Mtn.		10,981'	Beartooth
87. Shepard Mtn.		10,979'	Beartooth
88. Garfield Mtn.		10,961'	Bitterroot
89. Unnamed	(e. of Rough Lake)	10,961'	Beartooth
90. Tunnel Ridge		11,960'+	Madison
91. Snowy Peak		10,950'	Beartooth
92. Unnamed	(w. of Expedition Pass)	10,940'+	Madison
93. Black Mtn.		10,941'	Absaroka
94. Iddings Peak		10,936'	Crazy
95. Emigrant Peak		10,921'	Absaroka
96. The Needles		10,905'	Absaroka
97. Sphinx Mtn.		10,876'	Madison
98. Mystic Mtn.	(unofficial name)	10,876'	Beartooth
99. Saddleback Mtn.		10,876'	Beartooth
100. No Man Peak		10,843'	Madison

NOTES ON MONTANA'S 100 HIGHEST MOUNTAINS

The first attempt to catalogue the state's highest summits was made by Harrison Fagg of Billings several years ago in his "High Country Map of the Beartooth, Absaroka, and Northern Yellowstone Areas." This listed most of the 12,000-foot peaks in the state for the first time and gave unofficial names to many of them. (Official names must be submitted to and approved by the U.S. Board of Geographic Names before they may appear on a topographic map.)

The listing above is based upon a review of several dozen maps covering every major mountain range in Montana. It is difficult to identify with certainty all of the state's highest peaks because the only available maps for several areas (notably the Absaroka and Beartooth Ranges) are quite old and frequently inaccurate. When two or more maps were available for the same area (for example a U.S.G.S. map and a Forest Service map), elevations from the most recent map were used.

It is frequently difficult to differentiate between a distinct peak and just another bump on a ridge. The criteria we have adopted here list only those peaks that are officially named *or* those that rise at least 400 feet above the lowest point connecting them to an adjacent peak. This assures that only significant peaks appear on the list. Of course the best way to determine how distinct a peak actually is, is to climb it yourself. To our knowledge, no one person has yet climbed Montana's 100 highest mountains.

So for all of you real mountaineers, and you armchair mountaineers as well, here is the list of Montana's major peaks. Readers are encouraged to send suggested changes and descriptions of yet undiscovered peaks to Rick Reese, care of Montana Magazine, Box 5630, Helena, Montana 59604.

Special thanks to Cedron Jones for his exhaustive review of this list.

Next in the Montana Geographic Series

The Yellowstone River
High in Yellowstone Park near Younts Peak is born the last major free-flowing river in the contiguous United States. Undammed but not uncontroversial, the Yellowstone is the backbone of tens of thousands of square miles of southern Montana. It races through some of Montana's most rugged high country, creating a cold water fishery of international acclaim, yet as it flows from Montana the Yellowstone plods along laden with silt. It is no less important to the economy of southeastern Montana and no less cherished for its unusual warm-water fishery and diverse riparian wildlife. From west to east are communities as disparate as Red Lodge, Billings and Miles City, wild back country, irrigated bottom land, and miles of dry cattle country — all influenced by the wild Yellowstone.

Montana's Indians Yesterday and Today
Books abound on Montana's Indians in the past, but this is the first book to combine a colorful, accurate, concise history of the Indians that occupied what is now Montana and also to review the lifestyle, resource base, leadership and aspirations of Montana's Indians today. By William Bryan with photography by Michael Crummett.

Other Titles in Planning and Production
The Continental Divide——by Bill Cunningham
Eastern Montana's Mountain Ranges——Mark Meloy
The Rocky Mountain Front——by Rick Graetz and Gus Wolfe

MONTANA MAGAZINE
Tells The Whole Montana Story

The history, the wild back country, the people, the wildlife, the towns, the lifestyles, the travel — these things are Montana — unique among the states. Montana Magazine brings you the Montana story six times a year in a beautiful, long-lasting magazine.
Its hallmark is full-page color photography of Montana from the peaks to the prairies.

REGULARLY FEATURED DEPARTMENTS:
WEATHER
GEOLOGY
HUNTING
  AND FISHING
OUTDOOR
  RECREATION
HUMOR
PERSONALITY
GARDENING
DINING OUT

Montana Magazine
Because You Are
A Montanan

For subscription information write:
MONTANA MAGAZINE
Box 5630
Helena, MT 59604

Front Cover Photos
In the Spanish Peaks. (PAT O'HARA)
Along the Highline Trail, looking at Heaven's Peak,
Glacier country. (RICK GRAETZ)
Above the Absaroka-Beartooth. (RICK GRAETZ)
Beargrass. (LANCE SCHELVAN)